Anne Hooper, author ... a counsellor sp... emotional proble... Women's Sexual... orgasmic groups f... in the importance... women. She wrote ....en is based on her experie... .....en's Sexuality Workshop, in respon... ...pleas for help with sex problems from women all over the country.

Anne Hooper is the Wednesday phone-in problem counsellor for LBC Radio. An ex-director of the Forum Clinic, she is a member of the Association of Marital and Sexual Therapists and the British Association of Counselling. She has also written *Massage and Loving* and *Women and Sex*, while *The Body Electric* has been translated into several languages and is on sale in Europe, South America, Australia and New Zealand. Anne Hooper has three children and lives in London.

THE BODY
ELECTRIC

THE BODY
ELECTRIC

ANNE
HOOPER

Pandora

An Imprint of HarperCollins*Publishers*

Pandora Press
An Imprint of HarperCollins*Publishers*
77–85 Fulham Palace Road,
Hammersmith, London W6 8JB

First published in Great Britain by Virago Limited, 1980
First published in paperback by Unwin Paperbacks, an imprint
of Unwin Hyman Limited, in 1984. Reprinted 1989

Published by Pandora Press, 1991
1 3 5 7 9 10 8 6 4 2

The following sections of the book have
appeared, some in slightly different
form, in *Forum* magazine: *The Massage
Lesson* and *How to Give a Massage*, ©
Forum magazine 1976;
Self-Help and the Speculum, © *Forum*
magazine 1974;
and some of the *Fantasies*, © *Forum*
magazine 1975, 1976, 1978.
The fantasy on p. 87 is from *My Secret
Garden* by Nancy Friday.

Anne Hooper asserts the moral right to
be identified as the author of this work

A catalogue record for this book
is available from the British Library

ISBN 0 04 4408463

Printed in Great Britain by
HarperCollinsManufacturing Glasgow

CONTENTS

PREFACE

INTRODUCTION
How the workshop began 1

CHAPTER ONE
Week one 7

CHAPTER TWO
Week two 25

CHAPTER THREE
Week three 42

CHAPTER FOUR
Week four 60

CHAPTER FIVE
Week five 75

CHAPTER SIX
Week six 96

CHAPTER SEVEN
The four-week course 112

EPILOGUE
Group dynamics 115

AUTHOR'S NOTE

The characters of the women in this book bear no resemblance to any individual women who have taken part in this course, with the exception of Kate. Events and conversations have been taken from a number of these meetings to build up the composite personalities of the women appearing in the book.

This is the female form,
A divine nimbus exhales from it from head to foot,
It attracts with fierce undeniable attraction,
I am drawn by its breath as if I were no more than a
  helpless vapor, all falls aside but myself and it,
Books, art, religion, time, the visible and solid earth, and
  what was expected of heaven or fear'd of hell, are now
  consumed,
Mad filaments, ungovernable shoots play out of it, the
  response likewise ungovernable,
Hair, bosom, hips, bend of legs, negligent falling hands all
  diffused, mine too diffused,

Ebb stung by the flow and flow stung by the ebb, love-flesh
  swelling and deliciously aching,
Limitless limpid jets of love hot and enormous, quivering
  jelly of love, white-blow and delirious juice,
Bridegroom night of love working surely and softly into
  the prostrate dawn,
Undulating into the willing and yielding day,
Lost in the cleave of the clasping and sweet-flesh'd day.

This the nucleus – after the child is born of woman, man is
  born of woman,
This the bath of birth, this the merge of small and large
  and the outlet again.

Be not ashamed women, your privilege encloses the rest,
  and is the exit of the rest,
You are the gates of the body, and you are the gates of the
  soul.

The female contains all qualities and tempers them,
She is in her place and moves with perfect balance,
She is all things duly veil'd, she is both passive and active,
She is to conceive daughters as well as sons, and sons as
  well as daughters.

As I see my soul reflected in Nature,
As I see through a mist, One with inexpressible
  completeness, sanity, beauty,
See the bent head and arms folded over the breast, the
  Female I see.

I Sing the Body Electric
Walt Whitman

PREFACE

Since I first wrote *The Body Electric* in 1980, sexology has come up with new discoveries, and definitions, which affect pre-orgasmic women. Perhaps the most publicised discovery is the Grafenberg Spot, named after German gynaecologist Ernst Grafenberg. The G Spot, as it is commonly called, is described as a pressure sensitive area on the anterior wall inside the vagina. When pressed in the right way it triggers orgasm.

According to researchers Dr John Perry, a psychologist and Beverly Whipple, a nurse, every woman has a Grafenberg Spot. They also assert that part of the response during a Grafenberg orgasm is a type of ejaculation. The women who took part in their laboratory tests sent out a fine spurt of fluid from their urethra during orgasm. And, indeed, there is documented evidence on film showing precisely this.

What this substance may be, however, is surrounded by controversy. Perry and Whipple insist that it is *not* urine but a substance that corresponds to seminal fluid (without the sperm). Other researchers, notably Daniel Goldberg who has analysed the fluid and insists that it *is* urine, dismiss this claim. The argument has not yet been settled.

What is more, Israeli researcher Dr Zwi Hoch has carried out a six year study of the female genitalia and found that it is the entire area of the anterior wall of the vagina, rather than one particular area, that is richly endowed with sexual nerve endings.

What is important about this argument is that it brings back the old Freudian debate about clitoral versus vaginal orgasm. The difference about today's debate, however, is that no one would argue any longer about the superiority of one type of climax over another, as they did in the past. For the new research has indicated there are several sorts of orgasmic response.

However, what all these claims clearly indicate is that a variety of stimulation can result in a climax. This recently defined area inside the vagina may, for example, be responsible for the women (30 per cent) who are able to climax regularly through intercourse alone. Perhaps a large part of their arousal comes from the constant stimulation of the anterior wall by the penis. But the role of the clitoris shouldn't be forgotten. The Masters and Johnson theory that the clitoris acts both as a signal transmitter and receiver holds good. It is still a power house, receptive to an in-put of energy. Where that in-put comes from – be it the vagina or clitoris – doesn't matter. The fact that some women can fantasize themselves to climax without so much as moving a muscle, indicates that this very diffuse stimulation is enough to send messages from the brain to the clitoris with orgasmic effect.

If Perry and Whipple are correct in claiming that women ejaculate, this too has its repercussions. One estimate states that as many as 25 per cent of women who experience difficulty in climaxing may be hindered by a fear of urinating. Yet it is now becoming apparent that their experience may not be of urination but of ejaculation. Whatever transpires from this research, just the discussion of such possibilities as part of a normal response will help remove inhibitions for a lot of women. Perry and Whipple estimate that up to 40 per cent of women share the ability to ejaculate.

Perhaps the next most important change in how sexologists perceive the sex act today is in a new description of the sexual response cycle. In this book, in chapter four, the sexual response cycle is described in the way Masters and Johnson categorised it. Their original breakdown of the cycle into excitement, plateau, orgasm and resolution is a useful one.

But eminent New York sex therapist Helen Singer Kaplan has re-evaluated the sexual response cycle. She sees the phases as consisting of desire, arousal and orgasm. What on earth does it matter, you may justifiably ask, since the outcome remains the same? Which, of course, is right. But one of the important facts to emerge from Kaplan's observations is that although most women would hope to experience all three components of the cycle – desire, arousal, orgasm – these can each be experienced individually and are not necessarily dependent on each other.

The value of this to women with sex problems is that it gives us a better idea of where things may be going wrong. It explains clearly for the first time the example of the woman who is able to masturbate to orgasm with a vibrator, but who experiences *no excitement* of any kind while doing so, and very little sensation, apart from the feeling of contractions during orgasm. In Kaplan's terms, this woman is cutting out the desire and excitement stages and simply experiencing orgasm. As a guide for sex therapists this means that the woman is experiencing high levels of anxiety about her sexuality. In order for her to *feel* the excitement and rather more of the climax, she needs to work on why she is anxious.

Most skilled sex therapists would have perceived this in the first place, but nevertheless this kind of categorisation can be a help in visualising where to start on therapy. However, there is another very different line of sex research which throws quite a different light on to the problem of women who, try as they may, simply can't feel aroused and may or may not have an orgasm.

There's been some fascinating work done on sex hormones in recent years which indicates a possible proportion of women whose sexual response has been affected by a malfunction in their sexual hormone cycles. These hormone cycles are very finely tuned. How much of each hormone travels around your system is strongly affected by all the other hormones. If one goes wrong, so do several others.

Researchers now consider the hormone testosterone to be responsible for our sex drive. Women produce testosterone although not in the same quantity as men. The majority of testosterone in women is regulated by a substance called binding-globulin. This makes most of the testosterone sexually ineffectual. The small amount left becomes free-ranging (sexually) throughout our bodies. But a slight malfunction of one or several other hormones can be responsible for greater amounts of binding-globulin in the bloodstream which require 'feeding'. This additional amount of binding-globulin seizes the normal free-ranging testosterone and absorbs it. Since there is less testosterone available, our sex urge decreases.

A simple sounding solution is to re-balance the system by giving a calculated amount of testosterone either orally or by injection — unfortunately, easier said than done. But one study shows that 100 per cent of selected patients, carefully screened to ensure that this type of treatment was appropriate for them, showed a marked improvement when treated either with anti-depressants where there was a depressive element present, or with injections of testosterone.

The use of anti-depressants is interesting. They are prescribed on the grounds that depression, amongst other things, dampens the sex urge. In order to be sexual again the depression needs to be alleviated. The use of drugs is one way of doing this. But body therapy (not used in this particular study) is another. The massage carried out in women's sexuality groups often has a dramatic effect on raising depression, and the women in question become sexually responsive again. Depression may occur again at intervals after the course but follow-ups of two, originally very depressed, women showed that their experience at the course was the beginning of a series of self-help moves. One felt well enough to complete her studies for a degree and move on to a more comfortable lifestyle. The second started freelancing as an artist, left the mundane clerking job she had been stuck in for seven years, and emigrated to Canada to live near her sister. Although both were still subject to quite severe bouts of 'miseries', both learned to cope better and both reported longer periods of calm in between.

There is still some eight per cent of women who are not helped by any of the more usual pre-orgasmic programmes or one-to-one sex counselling sessions. It may be that this group of women will respond to hormone therapy. It's a relatively new way of treating women who lack sexual feeling but it may be an extremely effective answer.

Women come to sexuality workshops with widely differing problems and widely differing expectations of the group. I have learned to bring these expectations out into the open, right at the beginning of our sessions. When six or eight women offer an assortment of hopes it becomes apparent that many of these are unrealistic. An important note at this stage is to establish the principle that the sexuality group is a *starting point*. Even if the participants don't climax for the first time in four weeks flat (quite an ambition) they establish a basis from which they can continue to understand more about their sexuality and work on it.

One of the satisfying things that happens to me from time to time is that I get a letter from a group member of one (or even two) years ago who is thrilled to tell me that she has climaxed for the first time. For me, getting a letter like that is *my* version of job satisfaction.

Anne Hooper
1984

INTRODUCTION

HOW THE LONDON PRE-ORGASMIC
WORKSHOP BEGAN

My interest in helping women who have never experienced orgasm arose partly from hearing about Betty Dodson's work and reading her magnificent book *Liberating Masturbation*, and partly from the work that I do at the Forum Clinic.

Betty is a New York artist who makes huge, erotic pencil drawings of women. Through her drawing she became aware of women's sexual hang-ups and started to run what she calls 'Bodysex Workshops'. In these she teaches women to like their bodies and to masturbate by using vibrators. As a result of running the workshops for a couple of years she wrote her book.

I read it at the time I was running the Forum clinic for sexual and emotional problems and training there as a counsellor with one of our psychiatric advisers. Over my first ten months I'd been dismayed by the number of women who came to us who had never experienced orgasm. I was even less happy when I realised that no one was suggesting anything constructive to help them. It seemed to be only couples who *could* be helped (using the techniques of the American sex researchers Masters and Johnson) and this involved a long course of expensive visits to clinics. Betty's work was aimed at all women (married or single, heterosexual or lesbian). And her ideas were revolutionary.

On a trip to New York I talked to Betty and, fired with enthusiasm by our meeting, I resolved to start a women's sex workshop when I returned home. And sitting on my desk waiting for me when I got back was a letter from Eleanor Stephens. Eleanor had worked with women's groups at Berkeley University in California and had written about her experiences there in *Spare Rib*. She had been flooded with correspondence from women who were all anxious to do something – *anything* – about their sexual difficulties, principally lack of orgasm. Together we decided to found a practical work group.

We started in June 1976 with an experimental pilot of eight women, all with varying orgasmic difficulties. We made it clear that this was just as much an experiment for us as it was for them, so that there would be no false expectations. In spite of this tentative beginning, the course generated excitement from the start.

The programme lasted for eight weeks, and we met once a week for two hour sessions. Between sessions we had extensive homework to do, which we stressed repeatedly was vital to the course.

In the classes we talked about the kind of upbringing we received during childhood and adolescence, especially concerning sexuality. This is particularly important for women, who until recently have very often been brought up to think of themselves as inferior sexual beings, as a result of the sexist attitudes of their parents and society at large.

We encouraged each other to recall details of our parents' relationships, the ways in which we first learnt about sex (whether parents were covered with shame and embarrassment, whether they taught us to have sex, whether they were free and uninhibited). One interesting common denominator emerged; that the majority of women in this group were either only children, or had led very isolated teenage lives.

From upbringing we passed to the myths of sexuality, and above all the myths of masturbation. One girl remembered hearing that you 'weakened' yourself if you masturbated; another was convinced she'd once brought on an illness by masturbating as a young girl.

From the start we all opened up about our present personal relationships. Four of the women had regular partners, four had casual relationships.

We included a self-help session where we talked about the use of a speculum, the instrument used in the vagina to gauge a woman's 'internal' sexual health. One of us demonstrated how it worked, and showed slides of women's vaginas and interior pictures from inside a transparent speculum. The physiology of the orgasm was explained; what it actually feels like and how it happens.

From there we explored the possibilities of masturbation. We did not all masturbate together, as the women do in Betty Dodson's group. I suspect we would have frightened most of our participants away if we'd suggested that. But we happily set our friends a variety of 'pleasuring' homework.

First we encouraged them to have luxurious evenings where after a relaxing bath, making the most of bath oils, they would rest in a warm, softly-lit bedroom, and lightly massage themselves, all over the body.

The 'luxury' aspect was stressed since the point of the sessions was for the women to spoil themselves in a way they would not have previously considered lending time to. A feeling of luxury can be created even in very unpromising surroundings.

On subsequent evenings we said they should take the massage

further, exploring light and deep touches on the genitals, finding out which caresses were pleasurable and which were not. On no account was anyone to try to have an orgasm. This was simply self-touching for its own very pleasurable worth.

Later the genital touching became a more specific exercise for building up sensual energy. Regular bio-energetic exercises were part of the homework, and it was explained that the tension these caused in the thighs and pelvis were of great help in generating a flow of sexual energy.

Two points about orgasm were made clear from the outset. The first was that you are *not* physically relaxed while building up to orgasm. (In order to reach climax the pelvis arches, strains upwards and vibrates with sexual tension.)

Secondly, when concentrating on lovemaking with a partner who is trying to bring you to orgasm (be it through masturbation, intercourse or oral sex) it is vital to forget about your partner's needs in this sexual interchange and concentrate wholeheartedly on *your own*. Yes, it is selfish, but that ultimately is what sex is all about, where you disappear into an inner world of pure sensual adventure. Orgasm is a specific moment when it is impossible to 'think' anyway, let alone think about the all-pervasive needs of another.

At this stage, if the homework brought the women close to orgasm, they were encouraged to enjoy it. If, on the other hand, they felt they very nearly got there but didn't quite make it, they allowed themselves only half a dozen failures. Then, in order to keep their enthusiasm from dropping, we suggested that magical sex aid, the vibrator. The vibrator is often joked about or maligned. But it nearly always worked where masturbation hadn't.

It was Jean who first made a breakthrough. Jean had never experienced orgasm. Masturbating manually had been pleasurable, but she never felt she was anywhere near orgasm.

One evening, having newly acquired a vibrator, and *not* in a particularly relaxed mood ('I was snappy and irritable') she decided to try it out. 'In four minutes flat I was having explosive multiple orgasms. I smiled for a week afterwards!'

Another woman, Jill, had been fascinated with the self-help information; then, with the aid of a mirror and a torch, had made a careful inspection of her vagina. She bought a vibrator and began to use it. Every night after coming home from work she would lock herself in the bathroom and practice. First she felt distinct stirrings of sexual excitement. Later, she knew that immense sexual energy was building up, but she wasn't sure she was actually climaxing. 'I knew I was terribly excited but I somehow couldn't tell. I didn't feel awful and frustrated afterwards, though.'

One evening, before she was due at the group, she retired to the bathroom and, prior to practising with her vibrator, inserted her transparent speculum first. Having made sure she was comfortable, and watching her genitals in a mirror, she turned the vibrator on.

'The feelings of excitement grew as previously. When I reached a fever pitch of excitement, I could see in the mirror that my vagina was contracting; I could actually see, through the speculum, that I was having a climax. I counted the number of contractions. There were eight.'

Her lover was impressed but disbelieving. So in order to prove to him that she was actually climaxing she repeated her triumph in full view. From then on, they used the vibrator together in their love-making. As Jill grew more used to having orgasms, she began to feel them more fully, and enjoy the sensations.

The last session of the eight weeks concentrated on bringing the new-found ability to climax into our sexual relationships. Ways of communicating the idea of using a vibrator together were discussed. One woman had found it particularly hard to talk to her husband about her 'electric marvel' but she managed nevertheless. She was terribly pleased when, instead of being upset, he was sympathetic.

Another woman was exhausted by her boy friend continually pestering her for intercourse when she felt she needed time to herself. She managed to work out a system with him where on three nights of the week she could choose what they did, three nights he would choose, and the seventh night was left optional. Meredith therefore felt less pressurised by Michael. And we received a happy letter from her a month after the course ended saying 'Hurray, I finally made it.'

Those were the successes. A couple of women found it such hard work to masturbate to climax that they couldn't be bothered to try very often, but at least they knew they were capable of it. Another woman, it became apparent after about three sessions, used the group in order to gain other kinds of attention and not because she had a specifically sexual problem. In fact, she changed her story about her ability to have orgasms so many times that we ended up confused as well. It quickly became obvious she needed longer term psychotherapy which we couldn't offer. We suggested alternatives to her.

A fourth woman could masturbate to orgasm at the drop of a hat, but when faced with her boy friend could never 'come'. But when she described to us his aggression towards her, it was easy to understand why her body was refusing to respond.

At our final meeting we celebrated our eight-week friendship by having a marvellous lesson in massage. Bottles of jasmine-scented oil were produced, towels laid upon the floor and we took it in turns to massage each other. We all felt so good and friendly afterwards that we wished we'd done this earlier. It was a lovely goodbye.

Since that first group attempt, the group course has been much refined. It is now six weeks instead of eight and recently I've experimented with a four-week workshop. The youngest woman ever to take part has been seventeen, the eldest fifty-six. We've discovered that women want to do more physical body work than we'd ever imagined, and that the faster the group leaders lose their inhibitions, the sooner women new to the group unfold their sexual life histories. Several of us have been group leaders and we've tried to train new women so that they can start groups of their own. There are never enough workshops, demand always outstripping supply.

Part of the purpose of this handbook, therefore, is to give guidelines to those women who would like to start their own groups. It *would* be possible to overcome one's orgasm problems by doing all the work I suggest on the following pages in isolation. But it is far easier and more fun to work with other women in a self-help workshop. It's the experience of listening to other women's stories, swopping discoveries and sharing feelings which is most likely to lead to personal change. The social contact and pressure in the group is our greatest weapon!

We do need to understand that, as women, we alone are responsible for our own sexuality, its successes and failures. We must overcome old inhibitions and sexually repressive conditioning with first-hand knowledge of how our bodies function sexually. We need to understand how unfair it is to expect our partners automatically to know everything about sparking off our responses. The woman who knows she is sexually competent becomes confident about her own sexuality. And when *she* knows, she can get the message through to her lover.

This book takes us through a typical six-week workshop. Particular topics such as 'myths of sexuality' and 'the vaginal versus the clitoral orgasm' tend to arise at the same stage of each course. So I've added explanations for many of the queries that arise during a workshop. An index of these is made at the end of the book.

I have written the book to be as useful to lesbian women as it will be to heterosexual women. The reason I haven't included a lesbian character amongst the six women featured in the next chapters is because there have been no differences in the problems brought to our groups by the few lesbian women who have so far taken part. With the obvious exception of references to intercourse, everything written here about sexual upbringing, conditioning, knowledge and technique is as relevant to them as it is to heterosexual participants.

After the account of each week's course comes the homework. I make it very clear it has *got* to be done. There is little point in joining a *work*shop if you are not prepared to *work*.

As the weeks go by the behaviour of each woman subtly alters. Usually, by the end, she has achieved more self-confidence, certainly more knowledge and a more comprehending attitude to society, sexuality and men.

Week Six is a sad occasion. Emotional ties between us have become so strong that several of the groups refuse to disband. Long after the original course has ended, they are still meeting. One group persisted in learning massage skills, another brought their partners along for mixed meetings. There are always demands for an 'advanced' course.

Perhaps most important of all has been the rediscovery of the delight of masturbation. Masturbation, since Victorian days, has been deprecated successively as evil, harmful, draining the vital juices or, at best, a second best. In fact it can be a triumphant explosion or slow drawn-out ecstasy. It's a wonderful experience in its own right. It's free, fulfilling and simply requires the power of our fingertips (or occasionally the power of 40 watts). It beats *hell* out of the Archers, cocoa and early nights!

CHAPTER 1
Week one

Apprehensive glances round the flat, the smell of coffee drifting through the little rooms, and six women finding it hard to look at one another.

The grim, almost scowling nervousness of the first half hour of the first meeting has a lot in common with the prowling tension of a hospital ward before the op. But when the women say goodbye, at the end of their first session, their relief by contrast is almost joyful. 'I'm really looking forward to coming next week.'

As soon as people arrive we occupy them, giving as little time as possible in which to be fearful. They fill in a biographical sheet on which they tell us who they are living with (if anyone), how many brothers and sisters they have, the age at which they first remember masturbating, if they have, the number of sexual relationships they've had and, if they have a partner, his/her reactions to their joining the group.

They quickly drink the coffee put in front of them. Women are always late for this first meeting. They're scared. But at a quarter to eight we begin.

The eight of us (Jo assists me as well as owning the flat) are seated on cushions in a circle. So far there's been an embarrassed silence punctuated only by self-conscious remarks that quickly tail away. Now we break the ice with a rush. The women pair off and spend five minutes telling each other the 'facts' about themselves: why they are here, what they want from the workshops, what their background and family life is like, what they think about their parents and upbringing.

The room is now filled with talk and the women relax, gesticulate and begin to feel expectant, which is part of the purpose of the exercise. The other part is to prepare them for the next round, where facing the rest of the circle, they tell us all an expanded version of what they've just recounted to their neighbour.

JAN

Jan, aged twenty-eight, has come with a friend. She's a pretty woman, slightly overweight and possessing seemingly indiarubber limbs. She sits cross-legged in the lotus position and explains that she practises yoga. Jan can have orgasms through masturbating, has been happy to do this since the age of four. But she has *never* experienced an orgasm while lovemaking with a partner.

Jan's mother was warm and demonstrative towards her when she was a child. But her father was remote (he'd never touched her physically, either to hug or even to pat her). But Jan knew that he cared for her.

'I've a nagging feeling that I disappoint him, however hard I try,' she tells us. 'I constantly need to prove to Dad I'm a viable human being, that I really function, that all of me is there. But I suppose now I've given up a bit. And going through several experiences which were bound to antagonise him I've finally had to accept that I'm just very different from him. I'm trying to learn to feel all right with being me, instead of constantly feeling guilty that I'm not what *he* would like me to be.'

The experiences that Jan is talking about are those of becoming an unmarried mother (Luke, her son, is two) and living with the father of the child (Jim) without being married to him.

'I used to feel a lot of relief in being able to have orgasms through masturbating,' she continues. 'But now I worry that I do it too much, that it's becoming obsessive. And I'm scared there's something wrong with me as a woman because I can't have climaxes with Jim.'

How does Jim feel about it? 'He's never liked it. He used to complain at first. I thought it would help if I could say, "Look love, it's OK. I think you're marvellous, don't worry about the climaxes, I can get them through masturbation. Let's do it that way for me." But it didn't. "You're telling me I'm doing something wrong," he'd say continually. "You're telling me it's my fault, when it's not, it's yours." And I must say, I think he's right. I've had at least ten other boyfriends who've been lovers and I've never come with any of them either. I've never lived with any of them though, so it hasn't mattered much previously.

'We've been living together for three years now and the relationship has got pretty bad. There are lots of times when I think to myself "You'd be better off without him." But I just can't break it off. Firstly he's Luke's father. Secondly, I find him *so* sexually attractive I can't imagine ever finding any other man so marvellous to look at. And I don't want to do without that.

'I've got to a stage where I'm unhappy, I don't feel I'm important to anyone and my sexuality is withering away. I'm continually told by

Jim that no one else would be interested in me, that I'm a frigid bitch, and that he's doing me a big favour by staying with me. The trouble is, deep down, I think he's right.'

Further probing reveals that Jan is financially independent, has always worked, even after her child was born, is the owner of her own flat and is not supported by Jim. Since he tends to be in and out of work, she frequently carries him financially.

Her hesitant manner, halting, unsure way of presenting her problems and her immediately apparent desire to please are surprisingly at odds with her healthy, sexy outgoing appearance. It is as if she had all the ingredients of a very confident woman but could never learn the recipe to mix them successfully together.

LUCY

Sitting next to Jan is her friend, Lucy. Lucy is thirty-eight. She's tall, thin, and elegant. She gives the impression of being a high-powered career girl, whose life is organised exactly how she wants it.

In reality, Lucy is a competent typist but doesn't think she wants to do this for ever. She's working at a fashionable private London hospital, but hates the job. She has never experienced orgasm, has had a series of brief love affairs with men and has only had one permanent relationship during which she lived with a lover for two years. It has never occurred to her that masturbation might be a nice or a useful thing to do. She is an only child who has had very few close friends, either as a child or a teenager. Her father died years ago. Her mother is still alive, but lives in the country and Lucy does not see her often. In the past six years Lucy has had two nervous breakdowns, going home to live with her mother for a short time after the second. Now, she gets frequently depressed and is still regularly visiting a psychiatric social worker. She is shy and quiet, but when she is specifically asked for a view or an opinion, gives it confidently.

'I do have a boy friend,' she tells us, 'but he's not really a special boy friend. He's just someone to go out with. I don't think he's very interested in whether I climax or not. I'm here because I've realised it is ridiculous at thirty-eight actually not to do something about my lack of orgasms. And if I don't do it, I can't see that anyone else is going to do it for me.

'I'm very ignorant about sex. I want to know more. And I've come because Jan is here too. I probably wouldn't have come on my own.'

MAGGIE

Maggie too is a quiet, shy girl, aged twenty-six, single and without a boy friend. 'I lived with someone for five years and then he went abroad two years ago. There hasn't been anyone else since.' Maggie's life is full of activity in women's liberation projects and self-awareness workshop groups. It didn't sound as though she missed having a boy friend.

Her voice usually becomes very tiny and childlike when called on to talk, but when actually asked a question or contributing something she feels strongly about, it becomes far more forceful.

'I realise my parents have hardly any physical contact with each other at all,' she told us. 'They never cuddle or show affection towards each other. I think that's because there isn't much affection between them. My father railroads my mother in anything she ventures an opinion on and has no respect for her of any sort. He did the same thing to me until I was about twenty. Then I started standing up to him. We had dreadful fights. But however hard I argued I could see that nothing I said could win any change in his attitude towards me. To my father, women are a second-class sex. I gave up fighting.

'But I could and did leave home. The trouble with that was I hated leaving my mother to bear the brunt of his rudeness, and his lack of caring. At least my presence had alleviated his cruelty and had given her a sense of value as a mother. Of course now I'm frightened for her. I see her getting further and further inside her shell.

'It is hard for me to show affection. Joe (my boy friend) used to complain about the difficulties I found in giving him a cuddle. It wasn't that I didn't like doing it. It just never spontaneously occurred to me that it would be a nice thing to do. Perhaps that's because my parents never touched each other.

'I do masturbate, have done so ever since I was a child. But I don't seem to come. I get to a pitch where I'm very excited, I'm getting lovely feelings, and then it all goes away. I don't feel badly frustrated by it. But I feel there should be more to sexual life than a few faint tremors. Perhaps those actually are orgasms but if they are, they're a comparative let-down because they're nothing special.

'Perhaps I'm really climaxing but I can't let myself go enough to be sure. I did once think I had an orgasm when I was in a swimming pool but my boy friend said that would be impossible . . . I don't know what to think.'

MARY

Mary is a red-haired girl with a freckled complexion. She's wearing a maternity smock because she's still breast-feeding her five-month-old baby. Aged thirty, Mary has two children, the eldest three years old. Her husband is sexually very demanding, not just because he has a high sex drive, but because he equates making love with *being* loved.

And since he was starved of affection as a child, he demands it constantly from his wife now.

'Which means that every time I say I don't want to make love, he thinks it's a personal rejection. It's not. It's simply that I don't seem to want it as much as he does.' How often does he want intercourse? 'Every night.' Mary is not orgasmic.

'I've got to the stage where I'm feeling very angry about being constantly pursued by him sexually. I can't relax to enjoy myself in any way with him because the minute I begin to look happy he wants us to go to bed. I think I possibly could feel sexy if he'd let me have my own time. I'd love to want to make advances to him. But I'm never given the opportunity to want anything. He's always there looking hopeful.

'I love him. He's a marvellous man. We can talk about everything. But talking doesn't give us any ideas on how to change this thing. I don't want anyone else, because I have this fear that I'd be the same with someone new.'

Mary has never tried masturbation. 'Of course I know about it. But I couldn't do it to myself. Sex has always seemed to me something that two people should do together. Masturbating has seemed a "lesbian" sort of thing to do. And I'm certainly not gay.'

Why does masturbation seem a lesbian activity? 'Well, it's what women do to each other when they can't get a man, isn't it?'

Coping with two very young children has been a tiring process for Mary and as she describes her home life, a pattern of sexlessness emerges that coincided with pregnancy, young babies and fatigue. Additionally, it sounds as though her husband's need for affection is aggravated by the fact that she, like Maggie, finds it very hard to be outwardly demonstrative. 'My parents actually thought it was sissy to kiss and hold hands. I remember my mother once saying so. I certainly don't think it is, because I love someone cuddling me. But I don't seem to understand the right occasions when *I* ought to be doing the cuddling.'

HALEY

Haley is a twenty-five-year-old agency nurse, married to a social security officer. She's sexily dressed in a low cut blouse and is very vivacious. She and Len have been married for three years, have no children and are very open with each other over marriage problems and sexual matters.

'We go to bed often,' she tells us. 'We sometimes make love on the living room carpet at odd times of the day. He makes me feel very sexy. But I think I've only ever come with him twice. And each time the orgasm has been very faint.

'Len buys sex manuals and we read them together. I've taught myself to masturbate from them and I get very turned on by some of the "naughty" stories. But although the masturbation feels nice, I don't climax with it.

'Len has been very keen for me to come here tonight. He's very supportive. He hasn't had other lovers, but he did once help me to go to bed with a woman I fancied very much. He organised her husband one night (took him drinking) so that I could go to bed with the wife. It was very exciting. In fact we went to bed again on a couple of occasions. I still didn't come though.

'Len and I are very loving and cuddly to each other. When we're in bed together, sometimes I know I'm near to orgasm. But then part of me seems to turn off at that realisation. I find it hard to relax because I feel I'm being watched by Len. That turns me off effectively. I'm frightened that Len is going to be so upset by my not climaxing that in the end we'll split up. I love him a great deal. I don't want that to happen.'

KATE

Kate is thirty-four. She's a social worker and has worked professionally for twelve years. She is slight, and looks tired and drawn. Her clothes are colourless and when she speaks, her descriptions are halting. She has been in an on/off relationship with the same man for the past two years, and prior to meeting him had two serious love affairs, although she never actually lived with any of her lovers. She never masturbated as a young woman, although she did recollect masturbating publicly in a room full of adults as a child of four.

'I remember my father looking at me, looking as though he liked what he saw and then telling me to stop. That night I was waiting in bed for him to say goodnight and I tried doing it again. He came in and saw me. This time I stopped as soon as he came in. But he didn't say anything. Just kissed me goodnight and put the light out. Somehow I must have got the message that there was something dangerous in doing it. Because I don't ever remember doing it again. I became confused.'

It is quickly apparent that Kate still feels confused. Ian, her boy friend, refuses to make any permanent commitment to Kate, such as marriage. Having refused marriage, however, he proceeds to spend more time than ever with her.

'He expects me to be there to make supper for him and to be generally available. I know he occasionally goes out with other women, though he hasn't actually told me this. But if I ever breathe a word about the possibility of my dating someone else, he goes mad.

'I would quite like to marry him. But at the moment, I feel under-valued. He takes me for granted, as an appendage to himself. He expects to be able to come round and spend a night with me whenever he feels like it. But he doesn't bother to turn up if he doesn't feel like it. That would be fair enough if the same rules applied equally to both of us. But as far as he's concerned, they don't.'

Kate has been suffering from a lack of self-confidence that's been bad enough to send her to a psychiatrist for advice.

'I feel rather less than a woman, not being able to have an orgasm,' she explains. 'I finally decided I was quite old enough to do something about it. I felt pretty scared about telling the psychiatrist my problems. I feel terrified of telling all of you. He suggested I should join your group.'

During each woman's story I and the other women ask questions and offer suggestions. Participation from all members of the circle is encouraged. Very often an aspect of one woman's story will spark off recognition from another woman.

FAKING

When Mary mentioned she'd once faked orgasm with her husband, Haley confessed that she often did that with Len: 'Why did you stop?' she asked. 'And how?'

'I'd done it with a previous boy friend,' Mary explained. 'It hadn't helped anything and when I found myself doing it during the early days with Bruce, I forced myself to stop short; I confessed. He was, and is, marvellous about my lack of orgasm. I'm the one who's so fed up about it.'

'Why do you fake, Haley?' asked Anne.

'I don't want Len to feel he's not a success in bed. It's important to him to think of himself as a good lover.'

'But it's all right for you to go without a climax?'

'Yes – no. I don't know.'

'Had it occurred to you that by letting Len think you were satisfied by his methods of lovemaking you were *training* him to make love to you in the wrong way?'

That was a new idea for Haley. Having digested it, she then wanted to know what she should do about it. 'Should I tell him I fake?'

'How often do you do it?' Anne asked.

'About one in four times we make love. Certainly not every time. Len knows I find it hard to climax. What he doesn't know is that I've only ever had an orgasm twice with him.'

Some counsellors believe that the only way to make a marriage/partnership work is by making a clean breast of faking and starting anew. I qualify that by taking into account the whole marriage relationship and the depth to which faking is affecting it. In Haley and Len's case, owning up seemed unnecessary since the deception was only a minor one. Rather than risk an upset which might do more damage than good, it seemed preferable that she should wind down the faking so that eventually she could cut it out of their love life completely. Since Len was well aware she *did* have orgasmic problems, this wasn't likely to make much difference to their marriage. At the same time, getting Len to take part in some of the exercises that constitute our homework each week would enable him (and Haley) to know more about what actually did turn her on, and would take some of the performance pressure off her.

In a previous workshop, in contrast to Haley's case, twenty-six-year-old Ronnie confessed that she faked all the time with her boy friend, that he had no idea she couldn't climax and that she had lied to him about her reasons for attending the group. 'I told him I was keeping Jean company to provide moral support', she told us.

Ronnie was another woman with no self-confidence. She was pretty, petite, competent at her job, but she had got used to Tom making all the decisions for her and she had also got used to him taking it for granted he was doing her a big favour by his patronage. If she wanted to stick with him, Ronnie had to do what she was told. For two years Ronnie had done precisely that. She was non-orgasmic, although she did try to masturbate and had on occasion asked Tom to do it for her. 'He was very reluctant though,' she reported, 'and did a very heavy job.'

During the six weeks of the course Ronnie developed in two ways. Firstly she learnt to masturbate to orgasm using a vibrator. Secondly she realised through intense discussion with the group that her entire relationship with Tom (not just the sex) was a very poor one. With the support of the group Ronnie took the decision to reveal all to Tom. When she did, his reaction was so aggressive and unsympathetic that Ronnie, after a two-week verbal battle, asked him to leave. She managed to work out for herself that he was an unsuitable partner. The fake sex was, in this case, merely a reflection of the fake relationship.

Tom could have simmered down and, because he valued Ronnie, given thought to changing their life together. But he didn't. He simply was unsuited to her character and personality. And she used the group partly as a means of realising this.

TEENAGE SEXISM

Sex discrimination is sometimes so imperceptibly built into our lives that we experience it at the most impressionable times of our lives, often quite unaware of the damage it does to our responses as lovers.

Maggie was a particular victim of sexism in that her father discounted anything contributed by the women in his family. Only male opinion mattered. The result was that Maggie learnt from her mother that the best way to cope with men, or indeed with any serious subject, was to keep away from them or retreat into childlike behaviour.

'As a child I used to get on well with him,' she recalled. 'Then everything changed.' So today, if she feels at all threatened, she retreats. She presses back on her seat as far away as possible when she replies to the group. She fiddles with her long hair like a schoolgirl, and her voice becomes high and childish. In contrast, when she laughs, her voice is deep and rich, and when she's happy and excited, sounds contralto.

But we're all victims of sexism. From the time we graduate beyond childhood, girls are expected to be passive and acquiescent, boys the ones who take most initiatives. This is specially relevant sexually. A young girl who is promiscuous is thought of as 'fast and loose'; a boy is seen 'as a bit of a lad'. A male is expected to gather sexual experience so that he can teach his wife. A female is regarded with suspicion if she's sexually knowledgeable; 'she's all right for a good time but she won't do for a wife.'

Even in the technicalities of sex, a woman is often still expected to lie back and take what comes her way. (Irish Liz, twenty-three, mother of two; 'I've never really done very much in bed. I thought he'd know all about that. I mean, he's supposed to do all that foreplay isn't he? Yes I suppose I could do some of it to him but it doesn't seem nice, does it?')

The conditioning goes deeper than the technicalities. ('I can't have orgasms with him', says Margaret, aged thirty-eight and married to an Asian. 'But I honestly don't mind. He has a good time, and I always feel good seeing him satisfied.')

As women we are actually taught the pleasure of denying ourselves pleasure. We are often taught that it is wrong to feel sexual pleasure. Such pleasure is selfish, and as wives, housekeepers and mothers we are asked to supply favourable conditions for sensual enjoyment (eating, sleeping, hygiene, sex) of others. There isn't time for it for ourselves. Indeed, if we take time off we are being bad wives, housekeepers and mothers. Ours is essentially a caretaker role. Maggie, during her teens, always had to help with the washing up. Her father and elder brother never did. They simply sat down, read a newspaper or watched television. Now it is young children and the male who are encouraged to *enjoy*. Not so the female. Since *we* were once children, this breeds resentment. Some of us have excellent memories. So does our unconscious.

But sexism is not all one-sided. It works to the detriment of men too. Why should they always be the ones to take the risks sexually? By having to stick their necks out, making advances, they perpetually offer themselves up for rejection. And since it has recently been 'proved' statistically that men are the more 'vulnerable' sex (Michael Rutter, *Parent-Child Separation*, 1971), this seems to be especially hard on them. Why should men be expected to do all the work in bed? And how can men be expected to know the right formula for turning on a woman if *she* doesn't know it herself?

It is our responsibility as women to know our own bodies and how they function. When the function in question is sex, and its dysfunction has the far-reaching ability to disrupt the lives of partners and children, it is sound commonsense to do some personal research on our sensual responses.

Which means learning to masturbate. Masturbation is the act of stimulating the genitals (usually, specifically the clitoris) with the fingers or a vibrator or any safe object (eg. something unlikely to break and inflict injury) with the object of bringing on sexual arousal that may culminate in orgasm. And it's *never* too late to learn. Betty Dodson says that the definition of job satisfaction for her is teaching a sixty-year-old woman to orgasm for the first time.

SEXUAL MYTHS

Both men and women suffer from the false idea that all women have the same sexual responses and that as long as you carry out your foreplay strictly according to formula you can't go wrong: if by some freak of chance your wife doesn't respond to this, it means something is the matter with her. But just as our faces differ one from another, so too do our erotic responses; which means that to be successful in bed firstly you need to know your own sensual responses (exactly what kind of touch makes you feel good and where), and then there is the tricky job of getting this valuable information across to your partner. But it *can* be done.

Perhaps the greatest myth about sexuality is that the 'right' way to climax is through intercourse, and that any alternative way is immature, inferior: 'only for lesbians' (Mary) and unnatural. *The Hite Report* by Shere Hite (1978) is an account of women's sexuality based on 3,000 questionnaires filled in by women mostly from the New York area. In it, only thirty per cent of these women report that they can orgasm through intercourse. Whereas eighty-two per cent of the same women can orgasm regularly by masturbation.

This figure backs up that of the famous American sex researcher Dr Alfred Kinsey in his report on female sexuality (1953). And women everywhere are waking up to the fact that what seems to be the most 'natural' way of climaxing is *not* in the time-honoured missionary position under a bloke, but by masturbation – on your own, with your own lover or by your own lover, with or without penetration. And when you take that piece of sexological revelation and apply it to the bedroom routine a whole lot of worries and pressures fly out of the conjugal window.

Jan, on hearing this, realised 'that there's nothing wrong with me after all', which all of a sudden cast some light, or should I say blight, on her lover's behaviour. Kate who had been feeling 'less of a woman, not be able to orgasm', experienced a rush of self-confidence. Haley's reaction was 'so I'm not frigid'.

SELF-CONFIDENCE

A continual theme running through everyone's story in the groups is of feeling undervalued, ineffectual, lacking in self-esteem and self-confidence. Maggie, on mulling over the kind of belittling upbringing that she had experienced as a teenage girl, began to understand how her self-confidence had not only been undermined, but had never actually been allowed to develop. 'At least I do sometimes argue with Dad,' she said thoughtfully, 'and I *was* able to get out. Which was a positive thing to do. But then I think of my mother, who can't leave. She just sits there, retreating into herself, never speaking unless she's spoken to, and then he only talks to her if he wants something done for him.

'The trouble is,' she continued, 'I still don't know how to become effectual. I boil up with rage in an argument, but when I open my mouth to speak, anything I say sounds silly. It's better if I keep quiet. I didn't really want Joe to leave me two years ago, but there didn't seem to be anything to say that would be important enough to persuade him to stay. He didn't leave me because he disliked living with me, he went because he was offered a good job in India.'

Later in the workshop (weeks 2 and 3) we do an exercise that teaches us how to become more assertive. Today however we work out something to help in building up Maggie's knowledge and subsequently her self-esteem.

If, for example, she knows there are certain topics she can expect to argue with friends or family, she should swot them up beforehand and work out in advance the clear lines or argument she wants to take. By doing some research so that she knows what she's talking about she will have faith in herself in discussion. Because she has this faith she will find it easier a) to take part in the talks and b) to pursue whatever line she feels strongly about, instead of retreating into her little-girl shell because she thinks everyone else knows better than she does.

It's a long haul. It takes most of us at least the first twenty or thirty years of our life to become effective in verbal battle. Maggie has the added disadvantage in that instead of getting this kind of training from babyhood onwards, she is having to build up her self-confidence at the age of twenty-six. It shouldn't take her quite so long as it would a baby though, since she has already acquired a lot of basic skills and facts. It *is* hard work and unless you are one of the fortunate few who have a lot of confidence from an early age, there's no way round learning to acquire it.

What is the relevance of all this to sexuality? Your level of self-confidence, as a woman, is related to your determination to experience orgasm. Just as Maggie gathers facts together so that she is familiar with her arguments and can use them effectively, so too, do we need to know the facts about our sensuality and sexuality. This building up of our self-confidence helps us get ourselves past an orgasm block. Once past the block, our self-confidence increases even more rapidly, and we become more skilled at climaxing.

Of course, not all women are so 'put down' as females, nor do they have the same degree of sexual lack of confidence. But undermining women's sexuality is insidious. Take, for example, menstruation, something that affects every single fertile woman in the world (about fifty per cent of the population, in other words). Yet, until 1975, there was no book on the psychology of menstruation, and until very recently there has been virtually no thought given to the social effects menstruation has on the family, and relatively little scientific research into menstruation. (Happily there are now several books on the subject.)

In history, female sexuality as such hasn't counted for very much. In the past we have been valued as housekeepers and mothers, and as sexual objects for the pleasure of others, but we have rarely been looked on as sexual beings in our own right.

VALUING MASTURBATION

Learning sexual self-confidence, and thus to value yourself, leads you to realise the values of masturbation. There are some women who have attended pre-orgasmic workshops who have gained self-confidence as a *result* of learning to climax, while there are others for whom valuing themselves went hand-in-hand with *getting to know* that prize of sexuality, self-pleasuring.

Masturbation is the act of stimulating the genitals (usually, specifically the clitoris) with the fingers or a vibrator or any safe object (eg. something unlikely to break and inflict injury) with the object of bringing sexual arousal that may culminate in orgasm.

Masturbation is a delightful, fulfilling and restoring experience in its own right. It's a healer, an energy giver, an alleviator of tension, a gift of self-pleasure and it *can be* an ecstatic experience.

'Are you saying it would be all right never to have orgasm during intercourse?' asked Katherine, suspiciously. Katherine is a rather isolated housewife who lives in the suburbs.

My answer to her was that it doesn't matter in the slightest if you fail to orgasm through penis-vagina friction only. What does matter is that you should be able to orgasm in *some* way together. As well as being a sexual marvel in its own right, masturbation can also be used as a major part of lovemaking so that it allows an expression of love between two people. Many people equate making love with being in love and being loved, and to them it is important to reach orgasm when having sex together. But I would reiterate that as long as orgasm does happen, I don't think it matters in the slightest whether it's by intercourse, by masturbation during intercourse, by mutual masturbation or by individual masturbation while in each other's company. What does matter is that you are doing something lovingly together which gives you sexual happiness.

I once talked on a London radio programme about women's sexuality and answered listeners' phone calls on sex problems. One sad and depressed woman in her late fifties described a marriage of thirty years that had been totally without orgasm for her. The relationship had deteriorated to the point where the couple now had very little contact with each other at all socially, and none whatsoever sexually. Indeed, Mrs X and her husband had separate bedrooms. 'What is the use' this worn-down voice asked 'of learning to masturbate? It's far too late for it to be any good to my husband.'

'Blow your husband,' was my immediate indignant response. 'What about yourself?' Mrs X had had a lifetime of thinking her sexuality was something that existed simply for marriage. The thought that it was something existing primarily for *her* was very new. The idea that she, as a person, was important and that her sexuality reflected that importance was totally unfamiliar.

At least she rang off promising to try.

My outrage at Mrs X's desire to parcel herself away celibately until she conveniently departed this life was picked up by another lady listener in the same age bracket. This second woman had also endured a miserable married life. But three years ago her husband had died. To begin with she had forced herself to be outgoing, to cope with his absence. But she rapidly discovered that life was much more fun than she'd ever given it credit for. As well as making friends, she'd bought a vibrator and she had begun to have orgasms. 'I want to reassure Mrs X,' she said, 'that fifty-seven is not the end of the line, and that there's plenty left to live for. My advice is start now and make the most of the short time that's left.'

I am *not* suggesting we would be better off without partners. But I am saying we all have the means *within ourselves* to be sexually fulfilled.

Biologically, part of orgasm's original function was probably to encourage sexual encounters between men and women for the purpose of procreation. But I suspect that the delight of climax was given to both sexes *to keep them happy*, not just to make babies. After all, we don't *need* female orgasm to procreate. What do we need it for? I think climax was designed not just as a reward for copulation but as a safeguard against destructive aggression. It operates by relaxing our bodies when otherwise they might be subject to constant tension. Thus it has also been a biological means of making us easier to live with. And masturbation, as a prime means of experiencing orgasm, is a way, I think, of ensuring our survival through fostering happy communal strength, preventing our species from being dissipated and disrupted through built up tension and anger.

MYTHS OF MASTURBATION

Contrary to repressive folk-lore, masturbation does not make you go blind, deaf, catch 'flu, send you insane or kill you. If you happen to be male, the Victorian idea that each teaspoon of lost semen weakened you to the equivalent of a pint of blood lost is without any basis in fact, and if you're female, the suggestion that masturbation leads to concupiscence (unbridled lust) and nymphomania, is also untrue. The last belief, however, is interesting in that it may have been, in earlier years, the women with higher sex drive who dared to take these masturbation 'risks'. The same women may also have been the most active ones with partners, sexually, and therefore would have been open to sexual innuendo and slander.

'SECOND-CLASS SATISFACTION'

Mary has been fascinated by something Haley said about her husband's orgasms.

Haley: 'A lot of the time I've been satisfied by him coming.'

Mary: 'How do you mean?'

Haley: 'Well, he's had such obvious pleasure from his climax and he's been so loving to me as a result of it, that I've felt a pleasure and satisfaction through him even though I myself don't technically come.'

Anne: 'That's fine as long as you're happy with it. Pretty obviously, though, you're not or you wouldn't be here.'

Haley: 'I don't seem to be any more. Why do you think that is?'

Anne: 'It can be lovely enjoying someone else's orgasm, but not as a full-time job. And it's very much part of the passive wife-active husband syndrome. "The only right and proper way to be a sexual woman is through your partner". That's another sex myth.'

ORGASM MYTHS

Lucy: 'I thought that the ideal was for you both to have an orgasm simultaneously and as a result of this, experience a marvellous feeling of oneness.'

Anne: 'Like so many sexual happenings it *can* be great but the minute you start turning orgasms into 'ideals and 'goals' you alter the experience and you may ruin it. I've had simultaneous orgasms which have been lovely but leave me feeling flat afterwards. Whereas I've had orgasms, then gone on making love with my man until he has orgasmed which have been much better. It depends entirely on your feelings at the time.'

'SELFISHNESS' OF ORGASM

Haley: 'What about "Becoming one"? It sounds like some kind of sensual Nirvana.'

Anne: 'As I've said, there's no room in a climax for thoughts of others. You can't do it. It's a completely self-absorbed experience which focuses totally upon the sensual feelings in only *your* brain and *your* body. I'm not talking about the leading up to orgasm but the experience itself. When you climax you are far out in your head, going through wave after mental wave. You are not aware, while this is actually going on, of any of your partner's thought processes or of what he is experiencing. That's why orgasm has been compared to a "little death".'

Haley: 'But you do get a feeling of togetherness. I've felt that with Len.'

Anne: 'Afterwards, of course you do. You're as close and loving as two people can be and you've just shared a beautiful experience. When you're having sex with someone you love, it's about the ultimate in togetherness. But you can get those warm shared feelings however you manage to bring on the climax. You don't have to have intercourse to get them. You are *never* two people who become one, though. There are always two people, having two experiences, albeit at the *same* time.'

AUTOMATIC SWITCH-OFF

Kate: 'I get to a certain point of excitement and then something goes dead. Something inside my head switches off and stops me feeling sexy.'

Anne: 'You need to find out what it is that's making you do that. It could be childhood conditioning about sex being "dirty", or a fear of losing control, or an unconscious need to punish yourself, or a lack of sensual knowledge about yourself. If you are talking about lovemaking with a partner, it may be that unconsciously you resent him, or even that you are secretly distrustful of all males. It might simply be that you need to be more determined and carry on for far longer than you imagine is necessary.'

I don't go into a long analysis of each person's subconscious fears. But after talking briefly about them at this first meeting, most of the women leave looking extremely thoughtful. Part of their homework is to keep a diary during the course, which can prove invaluable for thinking back into one's past and working out one's actions and motivations. The emphasis is on doing the thinking for ourselves, not in having the answers conveniently provided.

WEEK ONE HOMEWORK

The homework for Week One includes a large proportion of bio-energetic exercises designed to re-awaken the energy flow around the pelvic area and to teach us how to generate tension there.

RELAXATION V. TENSION

The advice, given for years by GPs faced with female patients complaining of lack of orgasm, has been to relax. And although feeling relaxed when beginning to make love can be nice, it is not vital. What is vital is that when approaching climax the pelvic area is tensed. It is by building up tension, and therefore energy, that a reflex action, like a sneeze occurs, which releases that energy. Name of this reflex? Orgasm. So, if you consciously relax when hoping for a climax, you're doing yourself a great disservice.

Rather, exaggerate that tension, arch your back, push your pelvis up into the air, breathe in short breaths (level C of psychoprophylaxis training, a method of natural childbirth), tense your knees and thighs, wriggle and jiggle your genitals.

BIO-ENERGETIC PELVIC EXERCISES

Bio-energetics is a new therapy that uses an understanding of the body to heal the problems of the mind. By direct body work, using bio-energetic exercises, muscular tensions can be dissolved, leaving an increased physical and mental feeling of well-being.

1. Start with a *relaxation exercise*. Lie flat on your back on the floor (not a bed). Breathe in slowly through your nose and out through your mouth. As you continue it may help to let the breath out with a slight exaggeration (eg. say 'her' on the out-breath). After a couple of minutes start noticing, while you continue with the breathing, which

parts of your body remain tense. Try consciously to relax them. Begin at the tip of the right foot and work your way up the right leg, relaxing any part of it that may be tense. When you reach the top, go back down to the left foot, and come up that leg. Once you reach the abdomen, work your way up to your neck, relaxing as you go along. Then the right arm, next the left arm, ending up with the neck and the head. A good way to relax tense spots is to exaggerate that tension for a minute, by clenching the muscle, then letting go. Spend fifteen minutes on doing this. When you have finished this exercise, and after any other which involved lying on your back, make sure you do not sit up immediately, but take your time about it. In order to avoid letting the blood rush unpleasantly from your head, don't sit up with a jerk, but rather roll over on to your stomach and get up while facing the ground. This is a calmer and more peaceful method by which to rise.

2. *Grounding.* Stand with the feet firmly about eighteen inches apart, with the toes pointing in towards each other and the knees slightly bent, fists pressing into the back, just above the waist. On an in-breath let the head fall back and at the same time press the heels firmly down on to the ground. Don't let up this heel pressing. Hold this stance for as long as your neck and legs can bear it (breathing, incidentally, throughout) and when the time comes to stand up, do so on an in-breath. Once up, on the out-breath, let the top half of the body fall forward so that the tips of the hands are nearly touching the ground. And hold this, while still grounding those heels constantly. After a couple of minutes stand up and relax. You should, after carrying out the exercise a couple of times, start to feel a vibration in the tops of the legs. When you begin to be aware of this, you know the exercise has worked. The vibration signals the release of the energy flow.

3. *Pelvic Lift.* Lying on your back, draw up your knees so that your feet are squarely on the ground. Arms are along your side, palms down. Push up your bottom and arch your back so that they are right off the ground. Your body should only be touching the ground at the feet and from the shoulders upwards. You are actually resting on your shoulders. Hold this for a couple of minutes, then let your body down again.

4. *Pelvic Rock.* Lying on your back, palms down and legs flat, on an in-breath, arch your back (keeping your bottom on the ground) and let your pelvis fall away from the direction of your head. On an out-breath, press your spine to the ground and pull your pelvis towards the direction of your head. By doing these two movements on the in-out of each breath you will be aware that you are rocking your pelvis backwards and forwards.

5. *Squatting.* This involves squatting on the ground, with your arms

inside your legs, and your heels on the floor. Since most of us are not rubber-limbed contortionists it may be advisable to cheat at the exercise to begin with by putting a book beneath your heels. (Preferably a large one.) Hold on to something if you need to keep your balance. The object is to open up and relax the genital area while maintaining rhythmical breathing. Do for three minutes.

6. *Pelvic Circling.* Stand and move your hips in a circle forward, side, back, side around and around as though you are a hula dancer. Become aware of how you are breathing and ensure that, as with all the other exercises, you breathe evenly and rhythmically while you circle.

ADDITIONAL READING

Total Orgasm by Jack Lee Rosenberg, Wildwood House, 1974

DAILY SCHEDULE

Aim at doing one hour a day.

Day 1: Getting comfortable with yourself and your body. Take a bath, soap yourself slowly and caressingly, dry yourself and rub cream or lotion into your skin. (Baby lotions are good and cheap or, if you want, add a little perfume.) If you don't have access to a bathroom, just do the self-massage in your bedroom with cream. (Sit or lie on a towel to prevent the oil staining the sheets.) Notice the different textures of skin and muscle. Take your time, enjoy yourself, get to know your body.

Day 2: 'Talk' your way through your body in front of a mirror. Note down your feelings about yourself in a diary.

Day 3: Spend today concentrating on the exercises previously described (the relaxation and the bio-energetics).

Day 4: Write your diary. Repeat the breathing and bio-energetic exercises.

Day 5: Same as Day 1.

Day 6: Spend the hour indulging yourself, doing anything you like. Play music, dance, write your diary and focus on anything you want to discuss at the group tomorrow. It's important to spend an hour doing *exactly what you want* and not what *anyone else* wants you to do.

If you can find the time, it's a good idea to try and practise the relaxation and bio-energetic exercises every day.

CHAPTER 2
Week two

Everyone looks happier. Kate has washed her hair and is wearing a brightly coloured Indian skirt. Haley wears a dashing combination of soft woolly sweater and slash red lipstick. Maggie has brushed out her hair instead of pulling it back severely into a knot. And Mary has blossomed in a full-length emerald green smock.

HALEY

Haley is feeling particularly smug and starts talking about her experiences as soon as we've all arrived. Len has worked on a late shift most of this week so Haley has had clear time in which to practise her homework uninterruptedly.

'All that bathing and stroking. I've felt sexier and sexier. Last night, when we could do anything we wanted to please ourselves, was great. I lay down naked on the rug in the living room listening to the most emotional music I could find. Fantastic.'

MARY

Mary isn't so enthusiastic. 'It's impossible to make so much time every night. That regime simply isn't designed for busy housewives.'

Groans from me since it is *precisely* to fit in with housewives that we've tried to plan the homework. I explain. 'The whole point is that we don't normally spend enough time on ourselves. Therefore we've *got* to be more selfish. We've *got* to make time for ourselves. That way we begin to value ourselves more.'

We go into the practicalities of Mary's time. During the day it is obviously impossible to find an hour to set aside since the children are very active. But the evening has distinct possibilities. 'Bruce expects me to be with him at night,' she says.

I get heavy. I've discovered, from letting the homework ride in past groups, that the course doesn't work if homework is not adhered to faithfully. The women have to understand how important they are and *have* to find this time to spend on themselves.

Mary reluctantly sees the sense in this. 'But on the nights I did do it,' she continues, 'I felt funny. I kept thinking Bruce would come into the bedroom and I didn't want him to interrupt.'

'Lock the door,' we advise. 'It's the best way of knowing that no one is going to walk in.'

'There isn't a lock.'

'Then go out and buy a bolt. They're easy to fit.' Mary subsides in wonder. 'Can I really lock Bruce out?' 'Yes, provided you explain *exactly* why, provided that he understands.' 'Um. Maybe I will.'

KATE

Kate is sparkling with colour and confidence. 'I had things out with Ian at the weekend. It was a very hard and depressing thing to have to do. Especially when he said he had better move back into his own place. But instead of giving in, like I've always done in the past, I stuck to my guns. I felt awful seeing him go. I'd rather he'd said "let's get married and live happily ever after." But he didn't. And I can see that I've got to decide about my life. I'm convinced I did the right thing. I'm feeling really good about being so decisive.

'And it's changed my behaviour at work. I haven't been forceful enough previously and people mess me around because of it. But this week they haven't been allowed to. I've been clear and cool and I've insisted on having things done my own way. At a specially ferocious staff meeting today I stuck to the point I was making instead of giving way. I left with a lot more respect for myself.'

Kate's inner self appears to be reacting to her new outer behaviour. In the past Kate has had mild orgasms in dreams. Now she relates a new dream she had two nights ago. 'I woke up to find my vagina contracting violently. I think it was an orgasm but it was quite different from any of the others. It was so strong it was shaking my entire body.'

Kate is also getting very active responses when she does the bioenergetic exercises. 'My vagina contracts. It makes gasping noises. And I'm getting tingling feelings.'

STIMULATION RESEARCH

Research workers at New York University recently wired up equal numbers of men and women to record their physiological sexual responses.

When the people taking part were given erotic literature to read, all the men admitted to being turned on by it, which the monitoring apparatus confirmed. However, only half the women admitted to being excited by their reading *although the apparatus showed that they all were.* One conclusion to be drawn from the experiment is that many women are not able to identify or to tell the truth about their own feelings or arousal. So although many women deny being affected by sexual literature in the same way that men are, it now seems possible they are unaware of or actually suppress their responses.

MAGGIE

Maggie is far too quiet and I suspect she hasn't done as much of the homework as she ought. She lives alone now and has no boy friends so everything she does is very decidedly for herself. But she's keen-eyed as she listens to the others.

JAN

Jan has had very negative reactions on looking at her body nude in front of a mirror. Strange, since she has a beautiful skin and suppleness. Fortunately the others tell her this.

Jan's boyfriend has felt very threatened by her coming to the course even though she appears to be doing it strictly for his benefit. She tells us more about him – the more she describes him, the worse he sounds.

'I'm not surprised you can't have orgasms with such a bloke,' says Mary eventually. 'He sounds awful.'

He's a bully. He threatens her psychologically by telling her she's inefficient as a mother, can't be relied on and that if she doesn't watch out, she'll have Luke taken away from her and put into care. He bashes her for the slightest step out of line – that is, what *he* considers to be out of line, which usually coincides with her having an opinion that differs from his. He lives off her financially and contributes nothing to the household either financially or emotionally.

'Why do you stay with him?' asks Kate, in a daze.

Jan looks helpless. 'He's so attractive sexually. I can't imagine ever wanting to go to bed with anyone else.'

'But he's ghastly,' everyone groans. 'You don't need him.' Jan is thoughtful for the rest of the session. When we describe the YES/NO exercise which is part of next week's homework, she looks particularly contemplative. (See end of chapter for YES/NO exercise.)

LUCY

Lucy too is quiet. She doesn't say a word while anyone else speaks but when specifically called on for an opinion, talks volubly. Lucy has been thinking about the men in her life and she's not happy with them.

She's also begun to understand how basically ignorant she is about sex. 'I didn't know, till last week, that I could masturbate' she tells us. 'And I still don't understand about the clitoris.'

CLITORIS

The clitoris is an organ unique to women. It serves both to build up and to release sexual energy. It has no other purpose.

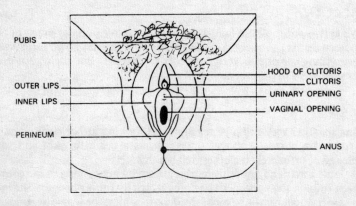

PUBIS

OUTER LIPS

INNER LIPS

PERINEUM

HOOD OF CLITORIS

CLITORIS

URINARY OPENING

VAGINAL OPENING

ANUS

Vulva—the outer sex organs.

All human embryos up to the sixth week of conception possess this genital bud of tissue and nerve endings. It is only after the sixth week in those children designated to become boys that male hormone sets to work and develops the clitoris into what eventually becomes the penis, a larger organ which also serves to void urine in addition to its sexual role. By stimulating the clitoris, by rubbing, stroking and caressing it, female sexual feeling comes to be generated.

We talk about the gaps in sex education for girls. Even in these days, only a few of the textbooks mention the clitoris. Most of them concentrate on the baby-making functions of sex. Most of the diagrams showing penis-vagina penetration depict the penis a million miles away from the clitoris. Small wonder it's hard to climax during intercourse.

Our clitoral anatomy is not designed biologically to come into easy contact with a thrusting penis. All six women say they think there is something the matter with where their clitoris is situated because 'it seems so far back', 'so high up', 'it seems to be buried under a mound of flesh', 'it's hard to get at'.

What they are describing are the normal sites for this estimable organ. Once the group understands this a certain air of relief descends upon the gathering.

CLITORAL STIMULATION DURING INTERCOURSE

'But that means it can be very difficult to come during intercourse?' says Lucy.

'That's right. Unless of course you use some other kind of stimulation at the same time.'

'What kind of stimulation?' she asks.

'A finger to touch your clitoris while you're making love. Either your own finger, or your partner's. And if fingers don't work, you can try a vibrator.'

Jan owns a vibrator, though none of the others do. 'It must be difficult to have the guts to take your vibrator to bed with you,' she says doubtfully. 'Doesn't your man think it's a put-down?'

'Try it and see. It can work very well. He may love it. He'll get some of the good vibrations too. Why not make sure that he does?'

TAKING YOUR VIBRATOR TO BED

Jo, my assistant, chips in. She tells the story of Sonya (a member of a previous group) who was determined to help herself to a more satisfactory love life by including her vibrator.

'She took it along, in her handbag, on the first weekend she'd ever spent with her new boy friend. After she'd been making love for a while and hadn't come, she said to him, "I'd like to have an orgasm. Is that OK with you?" "Well, yes," he was slightly bemused. "Have you got a light bulb?" she asked him next. His eyes bulged. What on earth was happening?

'Sonya wanted to plug in her mains vibrator. And so she did. Or rather, he did it for her. Then came the crunch. It didn't work. "I very nearly gave up," she told us. "But I was quite determined. I strode into the living room and tried it out on another light fitting there. It was OK. I triumphantly ran back to the bedroom and tried it there again. This time it worked there. And in spite of all the dashing about, he and I made love. It was lovely. He thought my vibrator was far out. I don't think anything like this had ever happened to him before."

'But there was still better to come. After they'd made love and talked for a while she instructed him, "I'm going to give you a massage. No sex," she added, "just lie there and take it".

'"The feeling of power that came over me was like champagne. I got drunk on that massage. It was a marvellous experience for *me* as well as for him."

'The upshot of all her directness was that she felt with this new lover she really was an equal. And for the first time she began to believe this relationship might work out well.'

SELF-IMAGE

One of the exercises in the homework last week was to look at ourselves naked in front of a mirror. Everyone, with the exception of Kate, disliked their nude bodies. There were resolutions to go on a diet, take more exercise and join a slimming club.

Why did they all think so poorly of themselves? Because none of them looked like a classic pin-up in the nude. It had never occurred to any of them just how unrealistic the currently fashionable female figure is. At present, there are two main ideals. One is still the very slim Twiggy-like figure, the other is the centre-fold girl, big breasts, slim waist and slim hips.

THE MEDIA NUDE

She's an image, an invention of the media, an unreal woman whom we have been conditioned to think of as the feminine ideal. Yet, if you look back through the history of fashion, you can see a variety of figures which, at one time or another, were all the ideal.

In mediaeval days it was thought beautiful and desirable to look pregnant. In Elizabethan days you were all the rage if you had square shoulders, and nowadays, in Mediterranean countries, large-bellied women are considered attractive. We thin, Northern outsiders away on holiday, can feel very unvoluptuous surrounded by well-rounded women who in their own culture appear beautiful. What I'm trying to say is that we're as beautiful as we feel, not as the media dictates. Kate agrees. She's flat breasted and likes looking that way. No one else is satisfied with the way they look.

How are these six women feeling now about coming to the group?

Maggie, who has remained mute so far, looks on the point of tears when she says how very supported she felt last week when everyone tried to think up ways to help her become more effective in discussion. It was quiet, pale Maggie too who blossoms in the next part of the evening when we go on to learn how to do a body massage together.

MASSAGE

Everyone has brought a towel this week and a bottle of sweet smelling massage oil. Good massage oil is difficult to buy but you can make your own quite cheaply by scenting baby oil with perfume.

'Let's get it over and done with,' says Kate, preparing for an ordeal. Maggie is rooted to her seat, paralysed with fright. But no one has to move yet because I do a demonstration first. At some workshops Jo takes her clothes off and I massage her. At others, I undress and she massages me. Either way, we've both learnt we must be relaxed about being naked in front of a new group. That way, when it comes to their turn to be nude, it doesn't seem such a big step for them.

Once I have demonstrated the massage strokes I become matter of fact and efficient. 'OK. Take a partner. Kate with Haley, Mary with Maggie, Lucy with Jan.' When they see that there is no way they're going to get out of it, they reluctantly take off their clothes.

But once their partner's warm hands slide firmly along their oiled backs the reluctance disappears. Now that they have been forced to have this experience, there is no alternative but to lie back and enjoy it. And enjoy it they do. The massage is transforming. They love it. They shed their inhibitions. They understand how daft it is to keep their pants on when they are so ridiculously in the way. They sit up afterwards totally unconcerned about their nudity. The women with lovers want to get back home and try the strokes out on them. Sometimes they feel so strongly about massage that at the end of the course they start their own massage workshop.

The greatest change tonight is in Maggie. She's no longer the tired little girl. Her usually childlike voice rings with a new decisiveness.

There have been two women at previous groups whose lives have literally been altered by massage. Lily was a twenty-year-old German girl who is a student in this country. She was so deep in depression she nearly committed suicide. She hadn't been near a man for two years because she was in despair at never being able to experience a climax. She had become convinced there was no room in the world for her any longer, that she was a sexual and emotional misfit, and she would sit, night after night, alone in her room, crying.

The day we did the massage with her group had been a specially bad day for her. (Earlier she had been on the phone to Jo, telling her that life wasn't worth living.) But that same evening, during the massage, she discovered first that she could actually tolerate someone touching her and secondly that the touch felt so good that she began to be hopeful. During the weeks which followed she changed drastically.

She bought herself new clothes, looked ten times healthier, lost her depression, and shortly afterwards stopped going to the psychiatrist she'd been seeing for years. She went on to use a vibrator and never looked back.

Heather was in another group. She was a thirty-six-year-old South African who'd lived in this country since she was twenty. She was suffering from a depression so stultifying she could hardly speak. She'd been attending group psychotherapy and subsequently one-to-one therapy for seven years. She lived on her own, never read, never watched television and never went out, except to her job. She sat in her bed-sitter, thinking and doing nothing at all year after year. Her job as a clerk in the post office required nothing in the way of talent or initiative and therefore she was able to carry it out like a robot. Her psychotherapist suggested she should join our group.

Heather was extremely reluctant to take part in the massage, couldn't see that there was any point to it and was terrified we should think her body was unattractive. 'I've got bad spots,' she told us.

Her spots turned out to be only in her mind. Her first massage made her feel wonderful. In the space of half an hour she had become amazingly relaxed. By the next meeting she had been out and had tried the vibrator.

'It blew the top of my head off,' she said simply.

When she left the course, she was still subject to fits of depression but she had also acquired hope. We last heard that she was more assertive and self-confident and that she was trying to change her job, towards something more creative.

What is the point of massage? First of all, it is a lovely sensual experience. Secondly, it forces us to accept pleasure focused solely on ourselves and *not on anyone else*. It provides one of the rare times when all other demands for our attention fade into the background as we enjoy sensuality focused on us alone. One of the most important lessons we can learn is to accept and enjoy that sensuality.

MASSAGE WITH PARTNERS

Massage also establishes new channels of communication with loving partners. (One type of massage is the basis of marital dysfunction therapy as practised by the sex therapy clinics of the National Marriage Guidance Council and popularised by the US sex researchers Masters and Johnson.) Often, women who have found it hard in the pre-orgasmic homework to touch and stroke *themselves* suddenly understand what they've been aiming at when they have a massage session later with their husband or lover.

Each lover gains valuable information about their partner's body. Just as some of us are ticklish on the feet and others are not, so, too, other zones of our body are either sensual or non-sensual.

I have a deliciously sexy feeling when I'm touched down the side of my body from the armpit to the hips. Jo, on the other hand, finds her good sensations are focused directly on her neck and shoulders.

It's important to know these sensual facts about ourselves, important to know the erotic geography of our own bodies. If we are familiar with these erogenous zones it will be all the better for getting the information across to our partner. And when he or she has received the information we are transmitting, he/she will consequently be all the better able to please us.

A massage in the group is usually such fun that we find it a glowing finale to the second evening together. In a haze of goodwill, we leave each other's bodies and, fortified by touch, plunge back into the outside world.

What follows here is useful both because it gives a powerful first-hand account of what it feels like to be massaged and secondly because it tells you, the reader, exactly *how* to swirl your fingertips confidently and skilfully over an expectant body.

THE MASSAGE LESSON

My local guru was practised in massage. I was anxious to experience at first hand the ecstasies he described, so I encouraged him to invite me round.

His flat has one immense room, furnished with low-lying cushions, mattresses and Japanese style tables. In spite of the sheer area, it is hot; most conducive to taking one's clothes off.

Soft, melodious Japanese music is played and I am invited to lie down on my stomach, on a thin mattress on the floor. He is wearing Eastern whites, a soft, loose, white cotton top, and tie-over white cotton trousers that have no fly. It's interesting how he's managed to create such an atmosphere of relaxation and luxury in a basic bed-sitter, with simplicity and very little expense.

I am offered a choice of oils, smelling of fragrances. I choose the least lurid and softest scented. I find it a little hard to undress in front of someone I don't know intimately, but try to make as if I am at the doctor's, so that the scene feels impersonal. But it isn't. Eventually naked, I hurry on to the floor.

His hands are warm, and he rubs the oil into them before transferring it to my body. 'Try deep breathing,' he suggests. 'Concentrate on making your mind go blank.' I obey. It isn't hard to relax. And apart from explaining what he is going to do, he dislikes talking. He says it distracts him from the attention he is focusing on me. The lights are dim, and even though I'm tense, it is already good to feel so concentrated on.

He is very experienced at massage, and to my untrained body, very good. He not only knows a great variety of hand movements, but he achieves a variety of sensations by using three different layers of pressure. So what starts off as an erotic glide over the surface of the skin, deepens into a tension loosener, which eventually becomes a precise burning feeling as if he were running a long finger-nail down inside my flesh. But he isn't – he's just using the deepest pressure of all!

He is aware of my tensions, where they are reflected, and at what kind of body layer they can be skilfully manipulated. Most important of all, he tunes in mentally to what my body requirements seem to be, and almost telepathically holds me just right.

At no time do I feel irritated, uncomfortable or in any way made uneasy. He makes a point of never taking his touch from me, even when he is applying extra oil, or having a rest.

It's when you are touched so confidently and so intimately that you become clearly awake to the lack of touch you experience every day. I never want him to stop, never want him to take his hands off me.

And when, after a timeless period, he decides he has done enough and does stop, I simply refuse to move, lying there, still ecstatic.

It must be amusing for him, and probably flattering too, to see what a powerful effect he has provoked. Certainly I arouse him. It must be virtually impossible to touch a woman with every skill imaginable, to see her physical reactions, and hear her verbal ones, without becoming aroused yourself.

When early on he massages down my arms, culminating in deep palm-to-palm hand movements, his touch startlingly warm and sensual, I experience such powerful surges of love and affection that I don't want him to let go of my hand.

It is the friendliest, most loving physical sensation I have ever known outside sex in a love affair. I feel so good and happy just from this that I wish everybody could have a massage every day of their life!

I learn an immense amount about myself. I hadn't known how much I needed touch and attention. I could do anything if I was free to give and receive that kind of attention every single day!

It isn't just the physical sensation he engenders in me. It is the mental rapport, where I, with my physical reactions, lead him on to creating more and better stimulation so that I, in my turn, again become ecstatic, not just in the body but in my mind. The proof of this marvellous positive energy he has drawn out of me is my active desire to make him as happy as he's made me. So that when he finally finishes the massage, and we sit cross-legged on the floor drinking orange juice (after such an intimate experience, there are no inhibitions about being naked) I suggest I should massage him.

I am a little nervous in case my unsure touch should be an anti-climax after the mass of sensation he's provoked between us, but he is pleased at the suggestion. He is glad that it isn't only a one-way happening.

So he takes off his clothes and lies down in the firelight, and, oc-casionally receiving instructions from him, I go to work. It is quite amazing to know that you are provoking such feelings of sensual delight.

And the more I tune in to him and the pleasures he is receiving, the more daring I feel. I dare to concentrate on his erogenous zones, I dare to massage his bottom with confidence. (It's quite daunting faced with a strange bottom to know just how intimate you can and ought to be . . .)

His bottom turns out to be the most erogenous zone of all, so that I can touch him there, anywhere, firmly, upwards, downwards, make my hands swim in circles pull my fingertips deliberately over him, and whatever I do he reacts strongly, and sexually.

It is almost frightening, observing the kind of power I momentarily hold over this man. And learning from my earlier reactions, I know that having aroused him there, the rest of his body is stretching out, receptive to similar sensuality . . . If after half an hour I hadn't become so tired, I would happily have gone on for ever, for his benefit.

No, we didn't make love. It could have happened so easily after those hours of perfect intimacy. But I had inhibitions about that. I did, soon afterwards, on another occasion, teach my lover the things to which my guru had gently introduced me. And although neither of us had actually meant it to turn into a lovemaking session, that is what it became. By the end of one hour of massage, we were both so aroused that we made some of the most sensual love that he and I have ever made together.

HOW TO DO THE MASSAGE

Preparing a massage means creating a relaxed and receptive mood for the person. The sex of your partner is irrelevant to the details of erotofantasy you propose to conjure in his/her senses, so whether your lover is male or female, the sensual framework remains the same.

Dim the lights or light a candle, burn a sweet smelling joss stick or scented candle, make sure that you either have a pile of background records or a peaceful silence, and above all, keep it as warm as possible. Direct an electric fire towards your lover. Your lover should be naked, hence the need for heat. For if there is only a light draught, he or she may tense. The other vital factor to contribute towards initial relaxation is that you, the masseur, have warm hands, and that the oil you use has also been warmed by the fire.

Some masseurs like offering their friends a choice of oils. I usually use suntan oil, for the memories it brings me of summers, but my own masseur uses a choice of Indian flavoured oils, with exotic scents such as patchouli, ambergris, jasmine and musk. There is no reason why you couldn't make use of baby oil or even almond oil, if your purse won't run to anything more heady, but, in my opinion, they are not so good.

A bed may seem the obvious place to carry out your administrations but, alas, it's rampant with difficulties. A mattress 'gives' too much, your friend becomes slippery and 'bouncy', and you never quite know if he/she or the bed are getting the best deal. So it's the floor with a duvet or a sleeping bag on it to alleviate the pressure on the bones.

When you put on the oil, don't pour a little puddle into your hands and then slosh it in the direction of your victim. Even if it is warm, which I emphasise again is vital, the shock of having this dripped or dropped on the apprehensive flesh is considerable.

Rub it into your own hands before you transfer it with quick, matter-of-fact strokes, to your lover's back. I am assuming we are starting off by massaging the back because it is the easiest area to get access to without embarrassment.

Cover the entire area to be massaged. And this includes the shoulders, the back, any part of the arm exposed, the hands, the waist and the buttocks. You can stop at the top of the legs.

As some of the strokes involve actually kneeling astride your partner, it is both practical and sensual to wear only briefs or pants on your lower half, and a loose stretchy garment such as a cotton teeshirt on your top.

Any time the oil wears off your partner's body, apply more so that there is no roughness or undue pressure on the skin.

Make sure that your hands are clean and that there is no dirt or grit on them. It is sensible to keep your nails trim so that you cannot scratch your partner.

Some of the strokes will naturally feel easier if done from the side of your partner, but others, mostly those involving travelling up and down the back, are easier if done from a straddle position, actually sitting on top of your lover's legs.

Do not be afraid of shifting around and making yourself comfortable. Simply keep one hand in touch while you move. And take things easy. It's far more sensual to be massaged slowly than to be rushed at like an old washboard.

1. The first stroke is to place the palms of both hands on the shoulders and move them in *circles*, firmly outwards and away from the backbone, progressing down the back, along the sides of the body, till you reach the buttocks.

Continue the circling on down the buttocks until you reach the upper part of the legs where you reverse the process and go back up the body.

When you return to the shoulders, encompass the top part of the arms, and end by returning across the shoulders to the neck where your thumbs should naturally penetrate the hairline, and perform a little individual massage of their own.

The circling stroke can be carried out over the back six times, and of course the pressure of the stroke can be varied. As you grow more experienced, your fingers will sense the depth that your friend will enjoy. On the last circling session, finish below the buttocks.

2. From there you can carry out the next movement which is the *glide*. I think this is the most spectacular part of any massage. Place your hands on the lowest part of your friend's bottom with the palms flat and the fingers pointing towards the head. Then, with the weight of your body directed from the solar plexus, start pushing both hands up along the spine, taking as long as you like.

Massage 2: 'the glide'

This is a heavy stroke as you are actually leaning on your friend. And your friend experiences this as a sense of overwhelming ripple, like a wave that flows directly along the back and threatens to engulf the head.

When you reach the shoulders and neck, lightly bring your hands down again to the buttocks and recommence.

It is important not to break your touch with your partner. If you have to apply extra oil, try to keep part of your body in contact.

3. *Swimming* is where the hands, using the palms, move in circles, close together, but in opposite directions to each other, taking on a kind of swimming sensation. This can be carried out up and down all the fleshy parts of the body, including the buttocks.

It is a good idea to include the buttocks as often as possible, as this can be the most erotic zone of the back. Touching the bottom can bring on prickles of delicious sensation to the breast, the head and the genitals.

4. The next stroke is aimed to eliminate the tension that many people experience in the lower back. Put your right hand on your friend's buttocks on the right side, with the fingertips on the waistline, towards the head.

Massage 3: 'swimming'

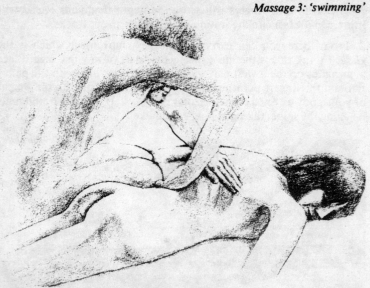

Place the left hand on top of the right one, then circle towards the hip, the side of the waist and around that lower back area, leaning your weight on to your hands. The giant circle that you make around this side of the bottom can be repeated four times and then carried out on the opposite side.

5. Working with both thumbs on the lower back, make short, rapid alternate strokes with each thumb, moving up the buttocks towards the waist. Carry this on up the right hand side of the body to the shoulders, repeat on the left hand side, and finish off concentrating again on the buttocks.

6. Sitting by your friend's side, place your right hand on the base of the spine, fingers pointing towards the head, with the left hand over it. Then slowly glide over the spine itself. This has a curious bumpy motion.

Come back down again at the same speed. But as you come down, dig two fingers into the indentations on either side of the spine, raising your right hand slightly so that the maximum pressure can be applied. Do these strokes three times.

7. Then go on to the *thumb pressure* strokes. By hooking the thumb into the space beneath the shoulder blade you can create a curious feeling of helplessness. This may be difficult to do if your lover is muscular and the best way to seek out the hollow beneath the shoulder

Massage 6: 'sitting by your friend'

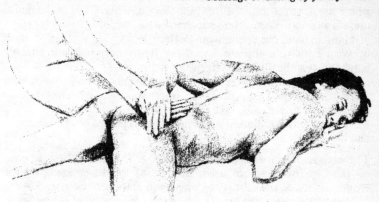

is to lift his or her arm up and fold it across their back. This brings the shoulder blade into sharp relief. Hook your thumb into the hollow side nearest to the spine and rake it through and out towards the armpit slowly. Do this three or four times, and then gently place the arm back on the ground, and do the same with the other arm and shoulder blade.

Massage 10: 'arms'

8. With both hands flat, fingers pointing towards the head, start at the top of the shoulders by pulling your thumbs, at a deep pressure, down the hollows on either side of the spine, till you reach the buttocks. You can repeat this exercise three times, on each occasion varying the pressure of your stroke.

9. When you reach the buttocks on the third repeat, make a variation of the glide by putting your full weight behind your thumbs and gliding heavily up your partner's back, and finishing in the hairline.

10. The arms. Rapid pulling strokes on one arm at a time with the whole hand, cover the area from shoulder to wrist. Once at the hand, there is a variety of small sensations to be sought for:

a) Hand to hand deep palming in circles.

b) With both your thumbs knead the fleshy parts of your friend's hand. This can be difficult if he or she is thin.

c) Very lightly and slowly, pull your forefingers down between each finger towards the palm, till all four finger spaces have been caressed.

d) Using the finger nails, rake the palm and wrist.

All these exercises should subsequently be repeated on the other arm and hand.

These ten strokes are the basis of a massage. The erotic effect depends on the type of pressures used, the use of the finger nails on the erogenous zones, the subtlety of where you place your caresses.

The strokes described here can be varied for the front of the body, the legs, the feet, even the face.

ADDITIONAL READING

Treat Yourself to Sex by Paul Brown and Carolyn Faulder (Penguin)
The Art of Sensual Massage by Gordon Inkeles and Murray Todris (George Allen and Unwin)
The Massage Book by George Downing (Penguin)

WEEK TWO HOMEWORK DAILY SCHEDULE

One hour a day.
Continue with the relaxation, breathing and bio-energetic exercises as before.

YES/NO exercise (three times a week). This consists of saying YES to three things you *really* want to do, and NO to three things you really *don't* want to do. For example, on one level, if you've been denying yourself chocolate because you believe you ought to be thinner, but you really fancy a bar, then have one, *if you're sure* it's what you want. On another level, one woman in our classes realised how much she wanted to burst out with anger when her lover was thoughtlessly and regularly causing her pain. Previously she had never dared because she was afraid it would upset the relationship. But with the YES/NOs she understood that if she came out with her anger as she wanted to, she might give each of them a chance to rescue the relationship. Certainly the relationship was getting worse for her by the repression of her resentment.

Day 1: Bath and self massage as before, write diary, paying attention to your reactions to last night's meeting.

Day 2: Using a small mirror, take some time looking at your genitals. See if you can identify the different parts, such as the clitoris, the urethra, the labia. Think about your feelings. Do you like what you see? Do you like looking? End the session with the breathing exercises.

Day 3: Diary Day. Record your feelings about your body and genitals. Think back to yesterday and your thoughts on looking at your genitals. Where do you think your attitudes and reactions to your body have come from? Have they changed as you have grown older?

Day 4: Bath and self massage as before, spending more time today on the genitals and less on the body.

Day 5: Using your mirror, draw a sketch of your genitals. Remember to bring it to the next group meeting. Genital massage again. Try doing this while watching in the mirror. See how your skin reacts to your touch and don't be afraid of touching the insides of your labia (lips) with clean hands. Make sure you use a massage oil to make the movement of your hands easier. The inside of your vagina is actually cleaner than the inside of your mouth and it's a good idea to try and become as familiar as possible with how you look, feel and smell. Smell your fingers after you have been touching yourself, taste them too (there is, I repeat, nothing unclean about vaginal secretions). There was one sentence in *The Female Eunuch* by Germaine Greer that had more impact on me than the rest of the book put together: 'If you think you are emancipated, you might consider the idea of tasting your menstrual blood – if it makes you sick, you've a long way to go, baby.' Try it, and you'll see what Germaine Greer was getting at. Take a note of any changes in your sensitivity to touch. Most women are likely to feel most sensation around the clitoris, but you may get reactions around the vaginal opening, at varying levels of the vagina, and, if touched very gently and sensitively, on the cervix.

Day 6: Note down last night's sensations. Make a list of what you might want to talk about to the group. Indulge yourself for the rest of the hour.

Above all, think about the YES/NOs throughout the week. And make sure you don't forget to do them.

CHAPTER 3
Week three

Kate dashes in, bursting to tell of her YES/NO decisions. She can hardly wait for us all to assemble before describing her week. As she talks, it becomes clear that her sex drive is very bound up with her feelings of self-confidence and assertiveness.

KATE

'I've really thought about my options with Ian.' She's in deadly earnest. 'He's been in touch with me daily, constantly pushing me to live with him again. I don't think he took me seriously when I asked him to move out before. He obviously just thought it was a mood and that it would pass. But I've considered everything carefully and said NO quite firmly to our meanderingly living together. It wasn't easy to do, because a lot of me misses him and wants him around, but then a lot more of me can just see how he's been taking advantage of my easy presence. So I'm sticking to my guns.

'But . . . I also exercised a new option. And that was to say YES to our having sex together. I decided that even though I wasn't living with him any longer, I really wanted to make love with him. So we did.

'I'm very pleased that I stuck to my decision because it gave me a new freedom this weekend and some really nice things happened to me. I went to stay with some friends and on the Saturday evening the four of us, two men and two women, were lying around talking. I told them about the massage we did here last week and they all became very interested. I described how free I'd felt after it. I'd thought it was marvellous to enjoy being touched by other women and the whole thing just felt so good. So suddenly one of the men said 'let's try it'. And took his clothes off. I felt pretty scared when that happened, but excited too. I told myself this is something you want to do, so say YES to it. So I did. I took off my clothes, then the others did too and the four of us began to massage each other.

'I was pretty tense and strung up to start with. But once I was the one being massaged I felt much better. I relaxed and then began to enjoy it. We changed partners, men with men, women with women, and so on, and some of the time we just talked, funny little quips.

'From being a nervous, uptight little bunch, frightened of over-exposing ourselves to each other, we expanded our friendship in the nicest ways possible.

'It was surprisingly difficult doing a massage with friends. I suppose everyone is scared of spoiling an already-established pattern of friendship. But afterwards I felt a real sensation of liberation. I'd done something difficult and found out I could enjoy it.'

Shortly after the weekend Kate had another of her orgasmic dreams. 'I've been having problems with a girl at work who is my assistant. I knew I was going to have a confrontation with her on Tuesday and on Monday night I dreamt about the confrontation. In it I was saying very forcefully that "there were no two ways about it, I was having my holiday in June and hers would have to be deferred". I remember shouting this out while pounding my fists to emphasise my determination and then I woke up to find myself contracting powerfully in a strong orgasm. It was tremendous. And it happened *twice* that night.

'Next day, at work, there was no problem in telling her my holiday arrangements. I didn't have to argue or shout or stamp my feet. I was cool and decisive. I'm getting such a sense of satisfaction to know I can actually *do* things.'

HALEY

Haley too has been practising the massage, with her husband. 'I bought a copy of *Forum* on my way home from work,' she tells us. 'It's the first time I've read it. The train journey home went by un-noticed because I was so absorbed in the readers' letters. What really got through to me was the problems section. I began to realise what pressure we are *all* under to be good at sex. And just finding out I wasn't the only one who was "bad" at sex, took a weight off me. I didn't feel so alone.

'When I reached my home station, carrying the magazine under my arm, I went to buy a paper from the newspaper vendor there. "What's that you're reading?" he asked conversationally. So I told him, straight out. "Oh yes," he said, "I know that magazine. What do you think of it?" I found myself telling him I'd been having sex problems and that I'd already been feeling better from finding that others were in the same boat. "Oh yes," he looked interested. "I'm the same." And we got into a whole conversation about his problem which is impotence and my problem which I suppose is an equivalent and I just thought the whole exchange was fantastic. I can't ever imagine previously having an intimate conversation about my sexuality with a newspaper seller. And I began to realise just how much I could open out too. You could definitely say that my being able to talk about *Forum* and sex to this man was a YES.'

Haley's journey home that night had a direct bearing on her massage with Len. 'I think some kind of pressure had been released by all this,' she said. 'Somewhere in my head, I relaxed. That night Len and I decided to do a massage together. I started off by massaging him, so that I could show him what I'd learnt. And then he did it to me.

'I lay on my stomach and he massaged my back. He straddled me across the thighs and began the glides and circling strokes up and down me. And he got very turned on by it. So did I. I began to make noises of excitement and he became so responsive that he got an erection. After about ten minutes of this his penis, which had been hitting me gently every time he bent up my body, just seemed to find its way into my vagina from that massage position. And very slowly, as he continued massaging me he also made love to me. I found it unbelievably exciting. Every stroke he made I knew I was getting a little closer to orgasm. Now usually, when I reach this stage of excitement, something inside me turns off. But on this occasion I felt open and free.

'And I knew, I just knew I could have an orgasm. We'd never made love in exactly this position before. And I think my clitoris was throbbing against the ground each time he pressed on me. I felt very high up and floating on my excitement. My orgasm was about to take off and fly away any second.

'What actually happened was that I was so near it, it may even have begun very faintly. But it didn't quite get there. The great thing, though, was it didn't matter. Because Len turned me over and made love to me with his fingers, and I came then immediately. But what pleased me so much was I suddenly knew that even if it hadn't quite happened, it could now. I'm sure I can.'

MAGGIE

Maggie, in contrast with Haley, is depressed. This week she hasn't done her homework. 'I live in a flat with a lot of other girls,' she says, 'and they're always wandering in and out of the bedroom. I know you're going to say I should lock the door but I think that would be a bit silly. They'd only start banging on it and wanting to know why they're not allowed in.'

It's the new confident Kate who points out the alternative. 'Hang up a notice, saying you want to be very private and that on no account are you to be disturbed until the notice is removed. There's nothing very difficult about that.'

Maggie has to agree. But then she says, 'I'm out all the time. I've got a yoga group twice a week, a woman's group on another night and I'm helping in a particular women's campaign at the moment which takes up all the other nights. There just isn't time. When I come home I'm tired.'

'You sound as though you're making difficulties,' says Mary reflectively. 'I can say that because I can see *this* week how I was *last* week. Don't you want to try and make this course work for you?'

'Yes, of course I do,' says Maggie defensively.

'Then you must do the homework,' I say.

'There doesn't seem much point,' she wails. 'The few times I've tried self-massaging and genital massage nothing happens. I don't feel anything. I'm ineffectual. I think I'd rather not start; that way I don't get all keyed up full of expectations.'

'Of course you must start,' says Kate, outraged. 'If you don't start, you'll never find out anything.'

Maggie begins to talk about her mother. 'I know that my mother's solution, in the face of difficulties, is to retreat. If my father gets mad with her, she never retaliates at all. And she never suggests any alternatives. All the suggestions about family activities come from my father. I've learnt from them that nothing *I* say and do is going to make much difference.'

Shouts from everyone assembled. 'Nonsense.'

'Your YES homework next week,' I say firmly, 'is to make time for yourself, put a notice on the door and persevere with the genital massage. Give yourself a fair opportunity in surroundings where you feel secure, to see what massage and masturbation feel like. It may be that you are somebody who will respond better with a vibrator, but it's sensible to try without first.'

Lucy hesitantly questions one of Maggie's characteristics. 'Why do you talk in a little girl voice?' she asks, 'when you feel you are under attack? Is it a way of fending off the grown-ups?'

Maggie is amazed. 'I didn't know I did,' she eventually manages to say. 'Do you think it matters?'

'Perhaps if you sound more grown-up,' Lucy suggests tentatively, 'people would begin to take more notice of you.'

Maggie says nothing else for the time being but retreats into herself.

MARY

Mary has taken the self-pleasuring part of her homework further than is suggested. 'I enjoyed doing it so much,' she says. 'Bruce was away for a week so I had a lovely clear time to myself. At the beginning I thought the self-pleasuring was going to be a waste of time and I got down to it very reluctantly. But the second night, something really clicked. I enjoyed it tremendously. I got very hot and very soft and had loads of different, exciting feelings in my vagina. I decided to see what would happen if I carried on. So I kept moving my fingers on my clitoris, and I came!' She beams around the group, proud of her announcement. We burst into spontaneous 'hoorays', 'congratulations', and clapping. Everyone laughs.

'The next night, needless to say, I was very keen to do my homework. It was a bit harder this time, but I could still do it.

'Which is all fine. But the trouble is, when Bruce came home I seemed to clam up. Not immediately though. The first night I was still sexy after these lovely feelings. For the first time in years I was quite keen to go to bed with him. Almost to show off I suppose. And it was all so new it was exciting for both of us. I decided to see if I could masturbate while he was in me and discovered I could. I came with him inside me which pleased him enormously.'

Mary doesn't look as if it had pleased *her* enormously. 'It doesn't seem to have solved anything between us,' she says wryly. 'I suppose I thought it would. But instead of letting him become more relaxed about sex, it's inspired him to up the pressure. He's on at me *all* the time to go to bed.

'The other night he did the ironing. I had had a hell of a day with the babies and I was exhausted. And although he too had had a tough day he did this work for me. Which was marvellous and I appreciated the help. But all the time he was doing it, I was aware of the thought, in the back of his mind, that "maybe if I do this for her, she'll pay me back by screwing me tonight". It's as if doing the ironing was a bribe or a barter of some sort.

'And since then I've been unable to come with him. To be quite honest, I've felt so *un*turned on, I haven't even wanted to masturbate.'

Ros was a girl in our first group who'd had a similar relationship. She had tried out the experiment of giving herself and her man certain nights on which they might or might not choose to have sex. Ros had Mondays, Wednesdays and Fridays on which she could say YES or NO to Mark about sex and Mark had Tuesdays, Thursdays and Saturdays. Sundays were optional.

What happened in practice was that Ros always chose *not* to on her nights, and Mark always chose *to* have sex and invariably they did as well on Sundays. Thus the amount of sex was cut by nearly a half.

'It gave each of them responsibility for their own nights,' I explain. 'Ros was no longer pressurised on her nights and Mark began to understand that her decisions were *hers* and not his.'

'That does sound like a good idea,' Mary is interested. 'Bruce might agree to that. Maybe I could suggest that to him.'

It dawns on me later in the evening that Mary has never talked about any other men in her love life. Must make a point of asking her next time.

JAN

'I'm not sure I have much to tell you,' she reports. 'I've thought a great deal about everything said last week about Jim. There are two things which, reluctantly, I've accepted. The first is that I *do* resent him but I realise I haven't let myself admit it before. And the second is that I've reached a stage of disliking him. That's in spite of still finding him attractive. So I find myself in a bind where I want to go to bed with him but then, when I'm there, the angry part of me turns right off him.'

'Could you, on a practical level,' I ask, 'manage without him?'

'Oh yes, of course,' she says. 'I already do in a way. He gives me problems, not help.'

'What about on the emotional level?'

'That's what I've been wondering,' she answers. 'I tried to work out what I'd feel like if he went away. There'd be a lot of relief. But there would also, be a scared bit of me that's saying suppose you never get another man.'

Lucy, her friend, chips in. 'I keep telling her she wouldn't find any difficulty in meeting another man. She just keeps saying "but he'll never be as attractive as Jim".'

'It's odd,' says Mary, 'because from the way you've described him he doesn't sound at all attractive. He may be outwardly, but he sounds like an unpleasant person inside.'

Jan looks very worried. 'I know. That's what I'm realising. But I still can't imagine getting turned on by anyone else.'

'Have you tried?' asks Mary. 'Going out with anyone else?'

'I've been out with one or two old boyfriends but I didn't really enjoy that very much. And I was scared of Jim finding out in case he got violent. He has hit me on a couple of occasions.'

'Does he hit Luke?' asks Maggie.

'No, quite the opposite. When Luke was born, he just sat in hospital and gazed at him. He didn't look at me, didn't speak to me, just drooled over the baby.'

'So he's a good father, is he?' pursued Mary.

'We-ell,' Jan doesn't quite know the answer to that. 'I thought he was going to be. But I've been realising that he has never actually spent any time with Luke. Although he thinks Luke is marvellous, the extent of his active interest in him is to tell me that I'm continually doing things wrong with the child. Which since I'm the *only* one who actively looks after Luke, is a bit much. He doesn't like the fact that I work (I do take Luke with me) says this makes me a bad mother, yet he doesn't actually go out and get a job.'

'You really don't need this man,' Haley has been listening open-mouthed, outraged.

'I'm beginning to see that's right,' agrees Jan despairingly. 'But how do I get him to go without dreadful scenes and how do I cope afterwards when he's gone?'

BREAKING UP

'I don't think you will be able to get him to go without dreadful scenes,' says Mary. 'I lived with a man for five years, before Bruce, who was a little like Jim. He was sometimes violent. And there was no way of busting up with him without terrible scenes. I got to realise after we'd nearly broken up on two occasions that I *had* to go through the scenes in order to be able to come out at the other end.'

'Did he hit *you* when you split?' asks Jan.

'Once. There were a couple of other times when I thought he was going to but he didn't. I became quite fatalistic about it. I knew I'd survive but I also grew more and more convinced he would have to go. If he gets bad, Jan, you can always get police protection. But I think it would be safest to be prepared for a bad time and act as if it's an emergency. Hopefully, you'll find you don't need to.'

'How did you feel when your guy went? Afterwards, I mean?' Jan asks.

'Incredible relief that he'd gone. My life was far easier and I didn't give myself time to miss him. I filled my evenings with things to do. I rang up old boyfriends, went to classes, got on to a party circuit. One of the best things was being able to spend more time with girlfriends. I got a lot of support from other women.'

'But I've got a kid. It's not going to be so easy when you've got baby-sitting problems to work out.'

'No. But it's not impossible,' Mary answers.

LIVING ALONE

'It's not the end of the world to live alone,' points out Maggie, who is doing precisely that. 'I thought I'd fall to pieces when my boy friend went abroad two years ago. But I've liked it. I feel self-sufficient now and I hardly ever get lonely.

'The worst bit is not having someone to give you an occasional cuddle, but I've done so many other things I never had time for previously. And *my* women friends were great too.'

MEETING PEOPLE

'If you're bothered about not meeting people, you could try advertising in the lonely hearts' section of your local newspaper. Lots of people do, you know.'

'You can't expect men to just drop into your lap,' says Haley, 'You'll have to take some kind of action. It may take time, of course, to meet someone who turns you on as much as Jim does. But if you don't date anyone, you'll never give yourself a chance to find out.'

Mary sounds jokey. 'You may get flooded with letters if you advertise. You could pass them around the group. We might meet some really gorgeous fellows.'

'That's not such a bad idea,' says Lucy, seriously. 'I might join you. If you advertise Jan, I will too. We could sort through them together.'

LUCY

On that optimistic note Lucy, always the last, gives her account of last week's homework.

'I'm not sure I really did the YES/NOs in the right way,' she says hesitantly.

'What did you do?' we ask encouragingly.

'Well,' she pauses for a while. 'I decided that I was fed up with my work. I've hated it for a long time, but I haven't actually done anything about it. Now I decided that I would. So I handed in my notice.'

Gasps from around the room.

'Then,' she continues. 'I realised how much I dislike living in my present flat and sharing it, so I went out and found another of my own.'

We're quiet now, awestruck, wondering what the next revelation will be.

'And then,' she concludes. 'I realised that the only reason I was going out with my boyfriend was so that I would have someone to go out with and that I didn't even like him. So I gave him up.'

Splutters and gasps from all around.

'Do you think they count as YES/NOs?' The amazing thing is that Lucy is still hesitant.

'I think they count as changing your entire life.' I'm stunned. 'You can't get much more decisive than that.'

The real surprise, of course, is that these momentous personal decisions are coming from the quietest and most unassuming member of the group. After the commotion has died down, Lucy explains that she's taking the risk of becoming a freelance typist while she makes up her mind what she wants to do full-time. When the excitement of her news abates we turn to another aspect of the homework.

We take a quick look at the drawings of our genitals which were done in the week. Then we talk about self-help and knowing your body.

SELF-HELP AND HEALTH

We talk about contraception, abortion, cervical smears, sexually transmitted diseases and the menopause. Each woman's experiences of these subjects is contributed, but since health subjects are dealt with so well in *Our Bodies, Ourselves* (see page 58) it is unnecessary to go into a lot of detail here. The group usually delegates one of its members to pay a trip to the nearest bookshop likely to stock these titles and bring back copies for everyone who wants them. Often it is worthwhile stocking up in advance on the relevant titles (they're all in paperback) and re-selling them at the meeting.

SELF-EXAMINATION

The finale of the evening is the self-examination. Using a transparent, disposable speculum, I demonstrate, with the aid of a mirror, some lights, a box of tissues and KY jelly (a non-staining, water-soluble jelly available from any chemist), just how to use it and why it's a good idea to do so regularly.

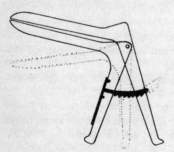

The unopened speculum is slipped slowly and carefully into my vagina until it has reached as far as it will go. Then I gently click it open. This enables me and the others to see inside my vagina, where the cervix is plainly in view at the end of the vaginal tunnel.

When everybody has looked and has gathered how to use the speculum, each woman takes her own from a store I supply

Speculum—closed and open

(she will keep it hereafter for her personal use) and, in turn, looks at her cervix, then demonstrates it to us.

Since it is often the first time that these women have had the opportunity to look at other women's genitals, this elicits reactions such as 'I'd no idea everyone's genitals looked so different. I'd always imagined they looked the same.' But like faces, genitals are uniquely individual. Betty Dodson's *Liberating Masturbation* illustrates this perfectly with her twelve superbly drawn pictures of different vulvae.

THE VALUE OF SELF-EXAMINATION

What, then, is the value of looking at each other's genitals and cervices when, in the past, these have been activities reserved mainly for the doctor?

The aim of self-examination is to demystify a part of the body that for hundreds of years has been kept a secret. Originally of course no one knew what the inside end of the vagina looked like, but eventually our midwives and doctors found out, and with the advent of modern equipment such as the speculum, it has become a matter of health routine to examine female patients (as for example, when you are expecting a baby). Yet a cervical inspection is something that generally tends to be done when you or the doctor suspects *something is wrong*. And what that leaves out is an interesting and positive realm of information that tells you about your body *when you are well*.

The New Women's Health Handbook puts this clearly into context.

'The intention of self-examination is to familiarize a woman with those parts of her body with which she has been denied familiarity. Underlying this is a responsibility for keeping her body healthy, a responsibility which a woman can choose to undertake herself, rather than abdicate to a doctor. This involves becoming conscious of the well body, so that she becomes sensitive to changes in her body which might indicate the development of sickness.

'When this is applied to most parts of the body, this theory is more or less taken for granted. We see our faces every morning in the mirror and touch them many times during the day. So we soon become aware of a swelling developing into a spot, or a change in colour or temperature. And yet when this is applied to the genitals many people react negatively. To some people a woman knowing her cervix and her vagina is too powerful a tool for her to cope with. Using a speculum, she might get an infection or damage herself, or she might get dangerously frightened or worried by what she sees. Or it might threaten her relationship with the medical profession. She might diagnose herself and not go to the doctor and the infection may get worse; she might waste the doctor's time by wanting to discuss and question what she has seen. And anyway, what's the point when she can go to the doctor and he'll look for her and tell her if there's anything she needs to know?

'Our answer to these attitudes is that a doctor does not see you often enough to know what is normal for you. He cannot always be sensitive to the subtle changes that would enable him to practise preventive medicine by detecting early signs of infections, disease and pregnancy.

'The politics of self-help are a challenge to some of the medical profession's attitude to our bodies; and they are also a challenge to the taboos which surround our reproductive organs, which alienate us from our genitals as being unmentionable, and under most circumstances, untouchable. Whereas in fact the genitals are an important functioning part of the body which we need to keep healthy. It is on that level that we learn to relate to ourselves through self-examination.'

Another value of doing a self-examination is to dispel fears we may have about our genitals. Betty Dodson thought for years that hers were deformed because her inner labia grew when she matured sexually and hung down like 'chicken wattle'. Her relief was great when she found out that hundreds of other women have the same shaped genitals.

For those who have been brought up to believe that touching yourself down there is 'dirty' it is a help to understand that the vagina and cervix are as much a clean, functionally useful and common-or-garden part of the body as are the penis and testicles on a man. No male would think himself 'dirty' should he pay hygienic attention to his genitals, and it is thought quite natural nowadays for little boys to explore themselves (although, sadly, even now there are still some who stop short of tolerating actual masturbation). Perhaps thinking along these lines will make it clearer to women that a natural curiosity about their genitals is healthy and that a knowledge of them is desirable since it is through this we may keep clean and well.

GROUP SELF-EXAMINATION

But why do a self-examination in a group? Why not just do it privately, at home? Of course, it is an excellent idea to do it privately. In fact, the best way to get to know the inside of your genitals is to monitor yourself every single day with the speculum over a couple of months, keeping a record of any changes you see in your cervix. This way you get to know what is normal for you at specific times of your monthly cycle.

But the use of doing the self-examination *together* is that it speeds up the delivery of information about what the inside of the genitals looks like. You may see a pregnant woman whose cervix will be a light mauvish colour, you may see a woman shortly before her period is due, whose cervical colouring will probably be angry-looking and her natural discharge perhaps faintly discoloured. Sometimes in the middle of the menstrual cycle, you may observe drops of blood coming from the cervix, which usually means that you are ovulating. You can see that some women possess a shorter vaginal canal than others, that the cervix may be located in a variety of positions, not always in the same place: but most important of all, self-examination is the most direct method of finding out that women's genitals are as uniquely different as their faces.

At no time should anyone be forced to do a self-examination if she can't face the thought of demonstrating herself publicly. But certainly it can be made clear at both this session and in the previous week that it is a valuable activity to carry out together. When six women trust each other enough to be able to do this, they experience warm friendship as a result.

I reproduce here an article written for *Forum* magazine in 1976. The material is based on an interview with Nancy MacKeith. She was the editor of *The New Women's Health Handbook* (Virago) now unfortunately out of print, and is the person mainly responsible for introducing self-help to this country and for encouraging the formation of women's health groups in England.

SELF-HELP AND THE SPECULUM

Self-help began in about 1968 in America, at much the same time as the Women's Liberation Movement began to get off the ground. Women at consciousness-raising groups decided they wanted to know their bodies, to demystify information about their health and sexuality, and that the key to all this was self-exploration and self-knowledge.

Carol Downer, one of the founders of the women's self-help movement in the USA, realised during her own gynaecological examination at the doctor's, that taking a cervical smear was so easy that there was no reason why she, and others like her, should not learn to do it for themselves. Founding a small women's group, she began to explore the use of the speculum. The small group idea snowballed until, today, there are many of them all over the world. Some of the biggest have turned into full-time women's clinics, where any female member of the public may come to seek information about herself. These clinics give family counselling and birth control – complete gynaecological examinations, cervical smears for cancer and VD smears are taken, and, in America, cannula abortions (or menstrual extractions) are performed. These clinics are organised on a fee-paying basis; the women run the clinics and get female doctors to work in them.

Some of the newest and most important information which has emerged for women has been through the use of the speculum. Regular and constant use on both well and sick women has led to knowledge that can be used as a basis for diet change, medical treatment, contraceptive advice, even cancer screening.

Nancy MacKeith is a former abortion counsellor, trained at the Los Angeles womens health centre, who has set up new self-help groups in England, explaining and demonstrating the use of the speculum.

USING THE SPECULUM

The non-pregnant uterus is about the size and shape of a pear. The big back end of the pear stretches up into the abdomen, but the small, narrow end (cervix) comes down into the vagina. When the speculum is used, it holds apart the vaginal walls, and exposes the cervix and the os.

The os is the entrance to the narrow cervical canal that leads to the uterus. Women who have not had a child have a small round os. Women who have had a child have a slit shaped one.

'Women who don't know themselves,' explains Nancy, 'have concepts of huge caverns inside them. They think they can lose a tampax in their uterus. If you've ever had that kind of fear, it's a fantastic relief to realize that it could never happen.'

INFORMATION GAINED THROUGH SELF-HELP

MENSTRUATION

'It is as safe to use a speculum during menstruation as it is to have sex. But women still need reassurance about this. In many women the os widens slightly during a period, presumably to let the blood out. This is why women are advised to have an IUD (coil) fitted at the time they are menstruating because then they don't have to be dilated so much.

'By examining yourself regularly you can follow the menstrual cycle and discover the days of your ovulation. This enables a woman to use an updated natural rhythm birth control method or to conceive if she wants to.'

MENSTRUAL CYCLES OF MORE OR LESS THAN TWENTY-EIGHT DAYS

'Since the Pill, more and more women have the idea that they are abnormal if they don't have a 28-day cycle. This is a result of the false 28-day cycle induced by oral contraceptives. We can show women that they are still ovulating on a three-week cycle or a six-week cycle. We do this by daily observation of the cervix. *After* a period the cervix is very clear with little secretion. Nearing ovulation we see a variety of secretions from the os. We can recognize the time of ovulation from the changes in the secretions.'

PREGNANCY

The cervix of many pregnant women becomes a veiny blue. Other visual signs are pigmentation around the anus, a line showing between pubic hair and navel, change in the colour of the cervix from pale pink to darker pink, increased secretion.

'We can diagnose pregnancy within a week of conception, provided we know what the woman looks like normally.' Nancy confirmed that she diagnosed her own pregnancy within a week. 'This is very valuable because you know immediately that you should stop taking drugs, should eat well, and should stop smoking.'

Nancy continued to view her cervix during pregnancy. 'As time advanced, the colour became darker and darker, and the secretions increased.

DISCHARGES AND SECRETIONS

The self-help groups identify these separately. A substance looking like egg white which appears at ovulation time or pre-period time is identified as a secretion. If it smells bad, or there is suddenly much more than usual, or if it is blood streaked, it is called a discharge.

White discharge lining the cervix is identified as 'thrush'. Many women don't realize you can have 'thrush' without having had sex. It may be due to a slight metabolic imbalance, or to being diabetic, being on the Pill, or eating too much sugar. Thrush can be cured by coming off the Pill, or ceasing to take antibiotics, or with an exterior local treatment of Nystatin. Self-help groups advise using yogurt, which they describe as a bland way of changing the environment of the vagina to make it unfavourable to yeast spores, which cause the itch.

Self-treatment is an aspect of self-help activities which stimulates adverse reactions from the medical profession. 'We could treat ourselves far more than we do,' Nancy explains. 'But we encounter such bad reactions from doctors that we don't. An example of this is with trichomoniasis. Doctors use Flagyl for treating it. This is yellow, and bubbly, and smells awful. It is also a very strong drug which can affect women, and especially the foetus, adversely. We have discovered that garlic can cure trichomoniasis but I know if I start recommending this, doctors will be outraged.'

CERVICAL SMEARS

'If, viewed through the speculum, a red patch is seen, it may be a cervical erosion. We would recommend that women should have a cervical smear, in case of cancer of the cervix. Although I must emphasize that an erosion is not necessarily an indication of pre-cancerous cells, a smear is a safeguard. In any case every woman should have one regularly, once a year.

'There may be a variety of reasons for cervical erosion. The woman may not be looking after herself by eating the right things. A change in diet can often clear up the condition. Eating more vegetables and meat usually helps. So can a local application of warm honey.'

IUD (COIL)

The use of a speculum enables a woman to locate her IUD, by making it possible for her to see the string dangling from the cervix. IUD users are recommended to check constantly that the string is still in place, as a guide to the safety of this contraceptive device.

Self-help groups have found that the cervix of many women with IUDs look unhealthy. Typical symptoms may be a small red patch and discharge coating the string.

There is no proven theory on how the IUD works, but certainly it irritates and disturbs the inside of the uterus, hence the extra discharge, and often infects it.

'I constantly hear from the newly pregnant woman who has been an IUD user that she had antibiotics around the time she conceived. It is possible that these drugs would cancel out the effect of the IUD, thereby removing the birth precaution, hence leading to conception.'

With this possibility in mind, self-help groups recommend that an IUD user takes additional birth control precautions while using antibiotics or even a lesser drug such as aspirin.

THE MYTH OF THE RETROVERTED UTERUS

Nancy MacKeith uses a collection of coloured slides to demonstrate interior anatomical differences. One of her slides shows a woman with the angle of her cervix tilted and the os looking up. 'The only thing that could be called abnormal by some doctors is the position of that hole (the os). In the textbook it would be looking straight out at you. When the woman sees 'retroverted' on her file and asks what it means, she is very often told 'it's twisted' or 'it's bent'. She may even be told that a retroverted uterus may make her sterile. The number of women who blame their fertility problems on that is astonishing. In actuality, there is no problem about becoming pregnant, because sperm can go round that slight bend quite easily.'

EXTRA SKIN

'Women often worry about extra skin – small flaps of skin outside or inside the entrance to the vagina. They may worry about one labia being smaller than the other. Self-help groups have found that most women have an extra piece of skin somewhere. *It's normal*. We also realize that most people have discrepancies in the size of their vaginal lips.

'I've given talks where women have practically fought to get down on the mattress first and have a look at themselves with the speculum. We use the transparent plastic sort, and with the aid of lights and a mirror, it is perfectly possible for every woman to see the inside of her own vagina and her own cervix.

'I find women are sick of lying down in a teaching hospital with 50 students peering up them, making remarks that they don't understand. They can't wait to look at this mysterious place where only doctors have been allowed to go.

'They like to find out that a pelvic examination need *not* be painful. They feel reassured, when after childbirth, they find that their interiors look surprisingly normal. Being able to view their own clitoris and urethra is reassuring.'

Women (and men) are afraid of the great unknown. The interior female genitals have for hundreds of years been a place of mystery. Women have had strange and sometimes frightening concepts of what is inside them. Now, they can see for themselves; a step on the road to self-knowledge.

Self-knowledge does away with fear and superstition and enables women to have self-respect. When you have self-knowledge it means you have potential control over your body.

HOW TO USE A SPECULUM

Before attempting insertion, assemble everything you may need for the operation, such as mirrors, tissues, KY jelly, light. The speculum should be lubricated with water soluble jelly (KY). The best position to attempt insertion is half-sitting, half-lying, propped against cushions, a mattress or even a wall.

The blades of the speculum are held together to avoid pinching the wall of the vagina and insertion takes place with the handle held upwards. After penetration is complete, the handle can be squeezed gently so that the ratchet opens the blades.

The speculum can be opened one notch at a time until the cervix is visible. In the textbook the cervix lies directly at the back of the vaginal opening. In actual fact it can be located at a variety of angles, and you may have to move the speculum around cautiously until the cervix and the os comes into sight. When you have finished viewing the speculum can be removed by pulling slowly and firmly from the vagina. It is not necessary to try to close it first.

It is not easy to juggle with mirror, speculum, and light all at the same time. It is therefore sensible, until you grow accustomed to using the speculum, to practice with a friend.

Speculae can be obtained from surgical suppliers in most major cities. The yellow pages telephone directory usually lists these.

Addresses of local women's health groups may be obtained from your nearest women's liberation group, and to find out where that is I suggest you get in touch with A Woman's Place, Hungerford House, Embankment, London WC2 or local branches of the Citizen's Advice Bureau. *Spare Rib* magazine also lists groups.

ADDITIONAL READING

Our Bodies, Ourselves edited by Angela Phillips and Jill Rakusen (Penguin, 1978).

Liberating Masturbation by Betty Dodson (Bodysex Designs) has recently had its title altered to become *Self-Love and Orgasm*. This new edition is available by mail order from the National Marriage Guidance Council Mail Order Book Sales Department, Herbert Gray College, Little Church Street, Rugby, Warks., for £3.75 plus 30p p&p.

WEEK THREE HOMEWORK DAILY SCHEDULE

One hour a day.
Repeat breathing, bio-energetics and YES/NO exercises as before. Add the Kegel exercises.

Kegels are routine exercises often recommended to women after they have had babies which are aimed at improving the muscle tone of the vaginal area. Named after their inventor Dr Kegel, many women have found that after about six weeks of practising the exercises, they experience increased pleasure during sexual intercourse. Exercising these muscles increases sensitivity in the vaginal area and also helps to reduce spontaneous urination with orgasm.

To find your PC (pubococcygeal) muscle, practise stopping the flow of your urine next time you go to the lavatory. The muscles that you use to slow down and stop the flow is the PC muscle. Practice stopping the flow several times in order to get used to it. Then lie down, and placing your finger into your vagina, squeeze the PC muscle again. See if you can feel the contractions on your finger.

The main Kegel exercise consists of squeezing the PC muscle for three seconds then relaxing it for three seconds then repeating this. Try doing this ten times, on three separate occasions every day.

The beauty of the Kegels is that no one need know you are doing them. You can do them while standing at the bus stop or doing the gardening or the washing up. The muscles surrounding your anus may also move at the same time, but if you find you are moving your stomach muscles or thigh muscles or your buttocks then you are squeezing the wrong muscles.

The second exercise is like the first except that you do it faster so that your vagina 'flutters'. It's a bit like a tongue twister in that you can't always be sure that you're doing it right. But as your muscles become stronger with practice, you should be able to 'flutter' more easily. Do this ten times, three times a day.

The third exercise consists of pretending that inside your vagina is a lift (elevator). Your job is to move that lift up your vagina, stopping at three stops on the way. When you reach the fourth and highest stop, you hold the lift there for a while, before carefully descending, again pausing at each stop, before reaching ground floor again. Try this twice a day. The fourth exercise consists of bearing down as during a bowel movement, but with more emphasis on the vaginal rather than the anal area. Try contracting the PC muscle, then bearing down in turn. Your vagina will open and close like a flower. Please note, all sufferers from piles and/or a prolapsed womb, leave this one out. Practise twice a day.

Constant routine practise of the Kegels strengthens the vaginal muscle so that, because your vagina is stronger, hopefully your orgasm will be too.

Day 1: Bath and self-massage. Genital massage as before, noting any sensations, however small, any changes in feelings, sensitivity to touch, pressure and rhythm.

Day 2: Continue with genital exploration, taking plenty of time; don't aim at having an orgasm, just pay attention to the feelings that you are experiencing, however small. The aim is to build on these, to slowly remake connections which have been disconnected and disused for ages.

Day 3: Examine your cervix with a speculum again.

Day 4: Read *Liberating Masturbation*.

Day 5: Bath and self-massage. Continue with self-exploration.

Day 6: Indulge yourself. Try and do the most sensual thing you can think of that you might enjoy. Prepare ideas for the group.

Throughout this week and indeed throughout all the weeks, make use of your diary. Record in it all your self-discoveries, your feelings and your experience of the group. Once again pay attention to the YES/NOs and think how to apply them to your everyday life.

CHAPTER 4
Week four

Week Four does not include any bodywork and comes as something of a disappointment. But since everyday life does not consist of a continual barrage of astounding and stimulating self-revelation, it's not a bad idea to bring the course back to more mundane reality. One of the saddest things I heard from one past member of the group – who had been lifted entirely out of a bad depression by the group – was that her life became an anti-climax once the course finished, and she developed for a while an even greater depression than previously. She did eventually overcome this, but it brought home to me the necessity of planting participants feet firmly on the ground prior to Week Six.

In addition, people who have been religiously practising the self-pleasuring homework and yet are getting very little genital sensation out of it (they always report good overall *body* feelings) begin to despair by this stage unless some practical alternatives are suggested.

Today therefore I introduce the vibrator. I do *not* believe it's a good idea to struggle on with only the muted sensations that some women experience during genital massage, since they lose heart. But neither do I believe that learning to touch and caress our genitals by hand is a step which should be left out. It's a vital step to feeling comfortable with our bodies and with sex.

VIBRATORS

I arrive at the meeting equipped with an assortment of vibrators and pass them around the room. There is the plain basic cigar shaped battery vibrator ('The Stimulant') which is the cheapest buy. There are the mains-operated models, made by two companies, Philips and Pifco, which are of course correspondingly dearer. There is a small pink ball-shaped vibrator called the 'Angel's Delight' which has only a very mild vibration but is sometimes more acceptable to women who feel the whole idea of a vibrator is infra dig.

There is a variety of more expensive battery-operated phallic models with an assortment of different heads but which do much the same job as the cheaper versions. There are several splendid and powerful Japanese/American mains-vibrators which are infinitely superior to the English models, but sadly, as yet, are not on general sale in this country, and finally there is the good old electric toothbrush. Yes, toothbrush – but, I hasten to add, the brush part, the bristles, are naturally all removed by you before you begin to use it at the opposite end of the body for which it was originally designed . . .

I usually provide a number of basic battery vibrators which the group may buy. Mail order addresses are at the end of this chapter. If someone prefers a mains-vibrator these are not available via mail order but can be purchased from any good electrical shop or store. I emphasize the desirability of using 'Long-Life' batteries with the non-mains models since they last much longer and they are more powerful. Very often when a battery vibrator seems ineffective it's simply because the battery needs renewing. And they wear out surprisingly quickly, which can be an unhelpful let-down.

I suggest the group uses the vibrators in their homework much as they've been using their fingers in past weeks. We don't dwell much on the subject but promise to discuss our experiences next week when we've had a chance to experiment.

LUCY

Lucy reports some sexy sensations while practising the Kegel exercises. 'My vagina feels wide open and yearning. If I touch or stroke my genitals after doing the Kegels for a while they feel very sensitive. At one stage when I was lying on my back doing them, I arched my back to lift my genitals up higher and my vagina gave a kind of gasp as though it were expelling air. Now, clearly every time I try,I can make this gasp. It's like a contraction.'

VAGINAL GASP

Not every woman is able to make the 'vaginal gasp' at will. It tends to be for those women whose body movements and muscles are well co-ordinated. But practising the Kegels is a good way of toning up the vaginal muscles and can help to build up sexual tension by getting your vagina to 'gasp' at will. It can be used consciously during climax to intensify orgasm and it can also be used to extend an orgasm. Some women, capable of multiple orgasms, purposely arch their pelvis after the initial climax while continuing with either self-stimulation or intercourse. They find that this sometimes triggers off another or several other climaxes.

Lucy is feeling pleased. Her boss has told her how sorry she is that Lucy is leaving her job. 'But it's come too late,' Lucy says. 'It's such a pity she couldn't have made me feel useful or wanted before. It's taught me how good it is to be openly appreciative of people. But if I hadn't been firm about leaving I'd never have wrung that admission out of her. So in future I'm going to let my contacts know how much I value them. It's also taught me that people do react forcefully and positively to strong self-confidence. I've been pretty ineffectual in the past, especially with boy friends. I know I'm going to be better off on my own at the moment than with a man I dislike. My resolution to give up Don hasn't wavered a bit. I feel I'm becoming a whole person for the first time.

JAN

'What's happened to your boy friend?' Kate asks Jan.

'He's still around,' she tells us. 'We've been having rows all week. The other night, when we made love, I did try to bring myself off while he was inside me. I've not tried this before, but I can see it could be a help. Jim, however, was very impatient with me. It upset him, he said, put him off his stroke. So in the end I just gave up and lay there. And that ended by making him angry. Finally he got up, put his clothes on and stamped out, saying he was going to find another woman who would behave more naturally with him, "more like a real woman" were his exact words.'

'Did he go to another woman?' we ask.

'Yes, because the next night we had a tearing row with me in tears all over him. I couldn't do anything properly, he kept saying, including making love. I wasn't a normal woman. And then of course he started telling me about a woman who did respond "normally". And it only took a bit more screaming at each other for him to come out with the fact that he went to bed with this lady last night, that she welcomed him with open arms and that they had simultaneous orgasms.

'I've been desperately hanging on to my own belief that I'm OK. *I* know I can function OK as a woman. It's been getting clearer and clearer to me why I don't relax with him. The more I think about him the more I can see why I've been living in a continual state of tension ever since I've known him.

'Thinking about the way I climax when I masturbate I can see the pattern of how I get turned on. I can come in about five minutes or even less if I want to. But it takes certain types of movement on my clitoris to get me going. I have tried tactfully with Jim, often, to get him to do some of these things to me. I have tried in the past showing him or doing it while he was fucking me. But every time it's been like coming up against a brick wall. I think he's frightened. I think he's terrified that this is a way of me saying *he's* ineffectual. So he gets in first with the accusations. It's hopeless getting good sex together with him. He blocks it off, he won't talk. So what can I do? There doesn't seem much point in going on.'

'What about being so attracted to him though?' asks Mary. 'Aren't you still feeling that?'

'Ye-es,' says Jan. 'But it's finally got through to me there's not much point. Nothing is going to work with him. He's not letting it. So, somewhere along the line I think I've switched off him. It happened when he stayed out that night.

'I still feel pretty hopeless about being able to fancy other men, but I've agreed to keep Lucy company in placing a 'lonely hearts' ad. Advertising is about the least I can do to get myself feeling independent again.

'And Luke's another matter. All this screaming and rowing is going on in front of him. And I know that's wrong, that it's hurting him. Jim actually picked him up and started thrusting him at me, saying I didn't care about him. And it's not true. I've been slogging myself stupid because I care for the kid so much. It's because of Luke I've been so reluctant to admit Jim isn't going to work out. And he's started using the child as a weapon which I think is a terrible thing to do.' And Jan burst into angry tears.

Immediately murmurs of comfort and concern come from us all. Jo fishes out a box of tissues and hands them to Jan. Lucy puts her arms around her and the rest of us back Jan, saying *we* think she's effective and caring and that she's an attractive and sexy woman.

KATE

Kate, particularly, is in great sympathy with Jan. She has been psychologically wrestling with her boy friend too, only in a rather different way.

'He still doesn't believe what I say,' she tells us. 'He's still trying to manoeuvre me into letting him come back to live with me. I know I'm doing the right thing by being firm with him but it's hard. He's using real emotional blackmail now. But if I let him come back we'll just sink into that unsatisfactory state where he treats me like a full-time wife while he opts to be a part-time husband. It may be OK for *him* but it isn't what *I* want.'

This week Kate looks tired and white. There are black rings under her eyes. 'He's saying now that he's beginning to realise he does value me. He's even throwing the word marriage into the conversation. And it's making it all so difficult. I *would* like to get married. And if I was sure that Ian meant all the same things about marriage that I do, I'd love to marry him. I can't tell you how much I want to believe him. But I'm not at all sure I do.'

'What do you want from marriage?' asks Haley.

'Well, children of course,' replies Kate. 'But there's got to be an equal partnership between us. I'm happy to allow Ian a lot of freedom in his life, provided I have the same freedom. What I just won't contemplate any longer is a double standard. And since that's what we've always had in the past there's got to be a lot of re-thinking on his part before we're going to reach my idea of a good marriage.'

She goes on to talk about using the speculum. 'I found it very hard to bring myself to put it inside me,' she says. 'In fact I'm still finding it very hard to feel OK about my genitals. I didn't like looking at them in the mirror much. I was certainly very interested to see you demonstrate the speculum last week but I was very scared to use it myself.'

How does she feel about the touching during the self-pleasuring homework? 'I can touch myself on the outside. I've got used to that. In fact, I like it. It's feeling good but not, I'm sad to say, orgasmic. But I still don't like putting my finger inside. It seems all wrong.'

How does she feel about her boy friend penetrating her during intercourse? 'That's fine. If it's someone else doing it to me that seems right. But if it's me, it seems wrong and dirty. I know it's ridiculous. I think I must have been slipped some powerful anti-genital conditioning somewhere along the line as a child. Maybe it stems from that time Dad saw me touching myself.'

MARY

Mary is nodding her head with fellow-feeling. Mary is the one who said that touching your genitals is a 'lesbian' thing to do. But Mary is also the one who learnt to masturbate to orgasm ahead of anyone else in the group.

'It was the massage,' she says, 'that changed my ideas about being touched. I was pretty appalled when I realised I was going to have to take my clothes off and be touched by other women. But I told myself "Now that you're here you might as well try it" and I forced myself to lie down. Then once the massage began it was so good that I didn't care who was touching me just as long as it went on. You could have massaged me all night and I wouldn't have minded. I don't know if anyone else felt like this, but I got very turned on. I simply hadn't realised how marvellous it is to be touched. And I reached a stage where if the person massaging me had included the genitals I not only wouldn't have minded it, I'd have adored it. And that was in spite of it being a woman who was doing the massage.

'And afterwards I felt so good and caring about all of you. We'd had this very intimate experience together and I hadn't minded. So it seems as if my feelings about women must have changed. I can't see myself getting drawn into a lesbian relationship but if other women want to I can accept how it might happen and I don't feel its wrong any more.

'After the massage I went home and practised the self-pleasuring properly for the first time. It finally made sense. I know I included the genitals rather earlier than you'd instructed but they felt left out otherwise.

'I find it extraordinary that I could have changed my attitudes so quickly, but I have. I'm beginning to understand how ignorant I've been about my body. I haven't known *anything* about it. It amazes me now that it's taken me all these years to discover it.'

Mary carries on to talk about Bruce. She repeats what she said last week, which is that she finds it impossible to get aroused by him.

'We have been trying out the contract you suggested last week. He thought that was a good idea. So far we've made love every night it's *his* night and never on my nights. Which is OK. At least it means I'm getting some kind of breathing space. And he has stopped constantly nagging me about sex, which is a relief. But try as I will I can't seem to fancy him.'

'Do you fancy anyone else?' asks Lucy.

'Well yes, that's the problem,' admits Mary. 'I'm constantly meeting men who turn me on. There are actually two chaps around who I'm having sort of affairs with. One is an old boy friend who's been around on and off for nearly four years. I go to bed with him occasionally. Bruce knows about him, even though he doesn't know I'm still going to bed with him. But I've never climaxed with John either, and I'm not sure I could. But there's a new man I met about two months ago whom I've seen a couple of times.'

'How do you feel about him?' asks Kate. 'Do you fancy him?'

'Yes, I do,' she replies. 'A lot. And now I can masturbate I'm pretty certain that if I get a chance to go to bed with him I could climax with him.'

'So where does Bruce fit into all this?' I ask.

'When I first knew Bruce,' she replies, 'I fancied him very much. But then I'd fancied the man I'd lived with previously a lot at the beginning of that relationship too. What I've been reluctantly realising is that there's a mechanism in me that, once I've become familiar with someone, slowly turns me off them.

'I can see that if hypothetically I moved in with this new man Keith, the same thing would happen eventually with him too. So there's no point in changing my man again. Anyway I value Bruce as a husband. He's a marvellous man in most respects. I like the kind of life I lead with him. I love our family. I know a lot of my problems revolve at the moment around the fact that I'm dog-tired from coping with two very young children. And he's immensely supportive with them. He does everything he can to help me. So it isn't that I'm itching to leave him. I'm not, quite the opposite. But what I have got to do is work out what to do with my sex urge as well as stay married. I know I've made strides by learning to masturbate.'

OPEN MARRIAGE

'Are you talking about opening up your marriage?' asks Haley.

'What do you mean?'

'Well, agreeing to be more open and honest with each other in your marriage, agreeing to give each other space, time off, allowing each other friends who may or may not be sexual friends.'

'In a way we do that already,' Mary frowns in concentration. 'I've known about the occasional times he's had an affair with someone else and he's known, to some extent, about my old boy friend.'

'You can both cope with that, can you?' I ask. 'Aren't you jealous of each other?'

'I was very jealous of him originally but since I've had the children he's made it so plain how much he loves me, I'm more secure now. I don't think our marriage is going to bust up.'

'Is he jealous of you?' I pursue.

'I think he was until he had an affair elsewhere. He saw that I wasn't going to leave him when I knew about it. And that made him a lot less insecure about me. You see, I do need him a lot. He gives me great security. And he knows that. So he doesn't feel insecure any more either. Which means that we've stopped being jealous. It's only the sex thing that's the problem.'

'What's it like when you make love?' asks Jo.

'It's not spontaneous,' Mary wrinkles up her chin. 'It's mechanical. I don't lie there like a lump, though. I move around quite a lot and I'm sexy for him. I like being sexy for him. It's just that even though we now know how to make me come it's still too mechanical to get me excited.

'He gave me two orgasms last week which were very nice but they've come a bit too late for me. I felt like a robot. I'm conditioned to *not* being turned on by him. When I look at him I don't see a man who excites me. I see the man who's spent all those years badgering me for sex!'

'It's only been a week of your new arrangement, for heaven's sake,' I say. 'You're not giving either of you a chance to re-adjust. You can't expect the relationship to change overnight. It may take you as long as another year or more to find a sexual balance. But at least you've begun. It sounds to me as though you've got a very good relationship which has needed for some time to be enriched by your getting something sexual out of it. You've made a great start.'

'You're probably right,' Mary subsides. 'It *is* early days.'

MAGGIE

Maggie too reports getting good tingling sensations in the genitals. She *did* hang a sign outside her door and her flatmates have respected her need for privacy.

'I've been talking to one of the women I share with,' Maggie tells us. 'She was very interested in the self-examination. We did one together on me while she held the mirror and the light. I'd like another speculum so that she can try too. We're going to monitor ourselves every day and keep a record of our body changes.'

This is the first time Maggie has spoken to anyone outside the group about her personal life. It is also the first friendly overture she has made to anyone. One of the facts that emerged when she first talked to the group was that although she is always very busy with her pressure groups and yoga classes, she didn't have any close friends.

Maggie has done her YES/NOs this week. She has arranged to go on a further course to learn more about assertion and how to gain self-confidence. She's asked her mother to stay with her in town, and not her father. 'It will give her a break. I felt guilty about not asking my father too but he wouldn't fit into my flat and he'd dampen me down so effectively that I and my mother would lose out any chance to be ourselves and be comfortable. So I decided to say NO to inviting him. I also determined to do the homework every single night this week, and I managed it. That's my YES. I feel very pleased about carrying that resolution through.

'I got some happy feelings from the homework. In fact,' her voice goes quieter and childish again, 'I might actually have had an orgasm but I'm not quite sure. I did get spontaneous waves of feeling but then they seemed to wither away and die.'

'Maybe you're on the brink but you can't quite let yourself go,' I suggest. 'Perhaps part of you panics when you get near to climax, and switches you off. Next time you reach this point *make* yourself go on with the stimulation and try to "open" your genitals to it. Think some sexy thoughts to help carry you into orgasm.' (Next week we will talk about using fantasy to aid orgasm.)

HALEY

Haley is low this week since she and Len have not been able to repeat last week's near-orgasm during intercourse. But she has stopped faking and is talking to Len openly about their sex life together.

'He's bringing me off every time with his finger,' she says. 'We're going through a really good time together. But I still haven't made it during intercourse.'

'Why is that so important?'

She stops to think. 'It's not as important as it used to be,' she says eventually. 'I feel better for being able to come at all with Len. Much better . . .

'Another thing we've been doing is my masturbating myself while he kisses and cuddles me. I can come like that too. Which is lovely. I can see I'm lucky to be able to do these things at all. It's just that I would like occasionally for us to both come at the same time while we're fucking.'

The second half of this week's meeting is devoted to a description of what happens physically to a woman's body when she has climaxes. It is based on research by Masters and Johnson but is interpolated with observations and gleanings from other women.

THE PHYSIOLOGY OF ORGASM

An orgasm has been described as a body reflex, akin to a sneeze. It actually is a physiological reflex which occurs as a response to sensual stimulation. It may be an all-over body response, it may be experienced solely around the clitoris, the sensations may suffuse the entire pelvic area, and the orgasmic contractions may be experienced in the vagina and the anus. Perhaps one of the most ignored features of climax is that as the body's responses begin, your brain temporarily loses control, and clocks you out to some kind of timeless state. But the main part of orgasm consists of rhythmic contractions emanating from the clitoris. Of course how and where orgasm is experienced is purely individual. Some women talk of overlapping excitement in their breasts or even their ears which they describe as mini-orgasm. Sex researchers would probably dismiss this description since they would argue the sensations were those of extreme excitement which can sometimes be confusing. But since these experiences are subjective, who's to say that these experiences are not orgasms?

SEXUAL RESPONSE CYCLE

The sexual response cycle is very similar for both men and for women. According to Master's and Johnson's classification system, each has four phases: the excitement phase, the plateau phase, the orgasmic phase and the resolution phase.

FEMALE RESPONSE
EXCITEMENT: The first sign of *the excitement phase* is vaginal lubrication. The vagina lengthens and distends and the vaginal walls change to a darker hue due to engorgement with blood. This blood engorgement, which in men is responsible for filling and elevating the

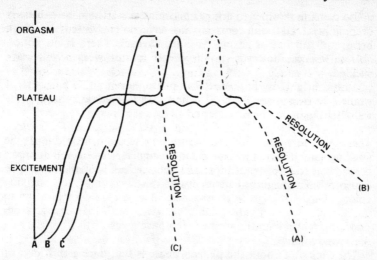

The female sexual response cycle.

penis, in women fills and elevates the labia and the clitoral shaft.
MUSCLE TENSION: During the late part of the excitement phase, many muscles become tensed, some of them voluntarily. For example many women tighten their anus muscles to heighten their stimulation. It is possible artificially to aid excitement by using the tensions and energy generated in the bio-rhythm exercises, such as arching your back, pushing your pelvis high into the air, and tensing your buttocks rhythmically.

Different body movements appeal to different women. I remember describing the Kegel exercises to a friend who gaped at me in astonishment. It wasn't that she was taken aback by the thought of exercising the sexual part of her body; rather, that for years she had been regularly rhythmically contracting her vagina as I'd described *in order to reach her orgasm.*

Recently I practised some bio-energetic exercises with a woman who confessed to being very scared of letting her body-energy flow in order to achieve the kind of body vibration we aim at. 'My body vibrates anyway when I masturbate,' she said. 'It's how I come. But I'm so ashamed of it I try and stop it when I make love with my present boy friend.' Perhaps not surprisingly she was unable to climax with him. When she described herself during sexual excitement it appeared that her entire body shook like a leaf to the point that her free hand danced around her hips involuntarily.

Another woman at the same bio-energetic class told us she lifted her hips rights off the ground during masturbation almost as if she were limbo dancing in order to achieve pelvic tension. The nipples usually become erect and with women who have not breastfed the entire breast will fill out as sexual tension increases. There is no noticeable difference, however, in the breast size of women who have suckled.

At the height of the excitement phase, seventy-five per cent of women develop a 'sex flush'. This is a measles-like rash that spreads rapidly from under the rib cage and all over the breasts.

PLATEAU PHASE: In the second phase of orgasm, *the plateau phase*, the outer third of the vagina now closes a little due to the swelling caused by the increased blood supply. Masters and Johnson have called this distended part of the vaginal wall the 'orgasmic platform'. The engorged inner lips at this stage undergo a striking colour change, though of course most of us are not in a position to observe it. In women who have never given birth they change from pink to bright red and in women who have given birth from red to a deep wine colour.

The tricky bit about the plateau phase is that during this level of increased sexual tension the clitoris, that key factor in all the excitement, seems to disappear. In fact, it is simply hidden in the folds of engorged flesh which arise around it. This doesn't usually matter if it's you who is doing the stimulating because you can still retain a fair idea of where the good feelings are, but if it's your partner, he/she has a tough time, since he/she is no longer certain if they are actually stimulating the right part. A little 'left hand down here' is a distinct help.

The tissues around the nipples swell with fluid so that the nipple erection also seems to disappear while the sex flush spreads to some or all parts of the body.

ORGASM: At the moment of *orgasm* (phase three) breathing is at least thrice as fast as it would be normally. An additional way of artificially building up excitement is by consciously speeding up breathing and making it shallower. Further, the heartbeat is more than double its usual rate and blood pressure increased by one-third. *Most of the body muscles are tense* (see Week One homework). No one has yet worked out exactly what it is that triggers the orgasmic response, but climax begins with contractions starting in the orgasmic platform in the outer third of the vagina. This platform contracts rhythmically as sexual tension is released. The contractions begin at 0.8 second intervals (see Masters and Johnson) and recur from three to fifteen times, decreasing in frequency and intensity after the first few. Sometimes the uterus contracts simultaneously; sometimes the anus.

There is an immense variation in women's experience of orgasm. A woman may have climaxes of different lengths and different strengths, experienced in different sites, both in the genitals and over the whole body, depending on her peace of mind and her physical state (eg. whether or not she's tired, happy etc).

Physiologically, orgasm is a release of the muscular tension and engorgement of blood vessels built up during sexual excitement. Subjectively, climax is a peak of physical pleasure. Aesthetically, it is what Marie Stopes described as bliss.

RESOLUTION PHASE: After the orgasm comes phase four, the *resolution phase*, when the body returns to its unstimulated state. Some women, most frequently those who have not had children, feel an urge to urinate. Many women do involuntarily urinate during climax. The best way to cope with this is to accept that it is a usual part of your sexual response and make provision for it by lying on a towel during lovemaking, or simply ignore it. The quantity is generally minute. One myth of sexuality has been that women, like men, sometimes ejaculate. This is not true but very often the slight involuntary spurt of urine can be interpreted as an ejaculation.

MULTIPLE ORGASMS
Where women differ from men in their sexual response cycle is that after they have reached orgasm, some of them, instead of rapidly going through the resolution phase, simply drop back into the plateau phase again, whence they can reach, either once, or several further times, more climaxes. However, please note, only *some* women are capable of doing this, *not* all. There is also one particular orgasmic response noted by Masters and Johnson which they call 'status orgasmus' in which a few women are able to have a rapidly recurrent set of orgasms with no intermittent plateau phase involved. Women who experience this may be able to identify the different peaks or may simply feel they are going through an intensely long drawn-out climax.

THE CLITORIS DURING LOVEMAKING
The clitoris plays a key role during sexual stimulation. It acts as both a receiver and transmitter of sexual feelings.

MYTH OF SEXUALITY
An old-fashioned misconception is that clitoris size is related to the intensity of a woman's orgasm. In other words, the bigger the better. Masters and Johnson in their laboratory experiments have disproved this. It doesn't matter what size your clitoris is, your orgasm will be as good (or as bad) as anyone else's.

INDIRECT CLITORIAL STIMULATION
The way the clitoris becomes stimulated during intercourse is not usually by direct contact with the thrusting of the penis, since,

anatomically, few of us are built so that the clitoris and penis encounter easily, but each time the penis thrusts in the vagina it exerts a pull on the labia. These in turn, exert a pull on the clitoris. So, indirectly, the clitoris is being stimulated throughout intercourse.

This argues convincingly the case for the clitoral hood. There has been a lot of publicity given to the 'hooded clitoris'; that which is so effectively hidden by the hood of skin over it that no stimulation can reach it. Surgeons have operated on women (and still do) to remove this hood thus facilitating 'better sex sensation'. In fact, there is only a microscopic percentage of women who actually need the operation. They are the women whose hoods are attached with some kind of lesion to the clitoris and who therefore cannot pull back their pubic mound to expose the clitoris. (A male analogy would be the man who could not retract his foreskin because it had grown attached to the penis itself.) But these women are *exceedingly* rare. For the rest, the imperfect 'hooded clitoris' is a myth. What these women need is less 'thrusting' and more masturbation. Usually when women can't find their clitoris, it's because they don't know it can be tucked up far inside the pubic mound.

If you do need direct stimulation on the clitoris, therefore, no operations are needed. All you have to do is firmly but gently pull back the pubic mound and the clitoris will roll out from underneath.

HOW WOMEN MASTURBATE
Every woman masturbates in a way that is uniquely and individually her own. Some women stimulate the whole of their genital area and not the clitoris alone. This takes longer to lead to climax but reputedly causes stronger and more satisfying climax than by clitoral touching and is less likely to be painful and irritating.

Some women find that the clitoris becomes painful when it has been manipulated too hard or for too long. They would perhaps react with more pleasure to very light finger-tip circling and twirling on the apex of the clitoris. Very few women manipulate the head of the clitoris directly, most often they stimulate one side of the clitoral shaft. For the female orgasm to continue its full length, stimulation *has* to go on until the climax is completed. *It doesn't carry on, on its own, without continued stimulation.*

SIMULTANEOUS ORGASMS
It has been stated before that this is an unnecessary goal and Masters and Johnson say that observing oneself during intercourse ('taking a spectator role') can lead to impotence or frigidity. Since it is easy to do this if you are trying to time your orgasm, it does sound as though there is a certain danger for some people in trying to come at the same time as their partner. However, for those people who've not

found it a problem, simultaneous orgasms of course can be good. Perhaps the best advice is that it doesn't matter in the slightest if you climax together *or* successively.

ADDITIONAL READING

Open Marriage by George and Nena O'Neill (Avon Books) is now out of print but probably obtainable from a library.
Understanding Human Sexual Inadequacy by Belliveau and Richter (Coronet). Available mail order from The Family Planning Association, Margaret Pyke House, 27 Mortimer Street, London W1 for £1.25 plus 36p p&p.

MAIL ORDER SEX AIDS

ORION Scientific, Dept. SR1, 23 South Bank, Long Ditton, Surrey.

WEEK FOUR HOMEWORK DAILY SCHEDULE
One hour a day.
Repeat breathing, bio-energetics and Kegels.

Day 1: Bath and massage. Genital massage as before.

Day 2: Continue with genital exploration. This time when you stop using your hands, experiment with the vibrator in the same way. If the vibrations are too strong and your clitoris is feeling over-sensitive, try using the vibrator through a soft towel or an Indian silk scarf. Try placing the vibrator on the entrance to the vagina, at the sides of the clitoris, at varying positions on the labia. Does it feel good if it is held very lightly over the clitoris, or is it better pushed against the clitoris very hard? Once more, don't aim at having an orgasm. You are simply trying to discover what kind of sensations you enjoy most in the genitals.

Day 3: Continue in the same way. Experiment with different pressures. Note down in your diary how you feel about this, if you feel any resistance to doing this, and how you think you might best overcome the resistance.

Day 4: As Day 2, but remember what has been said in the group about artificially heightening body excitement (page 69). See what deliberately tensing the pelvis, arching the back and breathing in a rapid and shallow way feels like.

Day 5: As Day 2. Bear in mind that ordinary vibrator batteries wear out rapidly. So if there is even a hint of less frequent vibrations, I suggest you change the batteries for new ones. 'Long Life' batteries last better and are also stronger. It's a good idea to buy a large supply at one go. That way you can change the batteries without having any kind of 'run-down' period. And it gets less embarrassing at the electrical shop!

Day 6: Write your diary. Prepare for the group tomorrow. Make a list of SHOULDS/SHOULD NOTS.

SHOULD/SHOULD NOTS
These operate in much the same way as the YES/NOs. Think carefully about what you feel you should or shouldn't do or be in your life and list them. These could be the 'I should be prettier therefore I'd better take more care of my appearance' or 'I should not be so fat, therefore I'll go on a diet' sort of imperative or, interpreted on a more everyday level, 'I should be a better housekeeper, career woman' etc, right through to 'I'm fed up with the oppression of women therefore I should do something active politically about it.' In other words the SHOULDS/SHOULD NOTS can be used on *any* level but whatever that may be, you will have to think carefully and conscientiously about them and then hopefully you will *do* something about acting on your resolutions . . .!

FANTASIES
If you use any erotic fantasies that make you feel sexy write them down and bring them with you to the next group meeting.

CHAPTER 5
Week five

Summer is here. Outside the weather is bright and sunny and the women bring a reflection of these fine days into the flat. They are all wearing colourful dresses, even Maggie who usually sports blue jeans. Kate has caught up on her sleep, Lucy looks unusually smug and Haley is bubbling with gossip and energy.

In contrast to the early days when at least someone would be late, today three of them are early. Jan, smiling and nodding, is swathed in floating cheesecloth and Mary, as usual, is calm and composed, her maternity smock a little crumpled and her long red hair floating free instead of pinned up in its usual bun.

In case any reader thinks observations about appearance are silly and unnecessary one of the first things that is noticeable during these workshops is the gradual transformation in appearance and mood throughout the weeks which exactly matches internal psychological progress. Week Five is an invigorating one. Homework has generated good vibrations and judging from the happy faces, there have been more than a few.

MAGGIE

'I have to confess I didn't do any more self-touching' she tells us. 'I tried out the vibrator the night of the last class. I couldn't resist it. I got back to my flat at about 11.30, and my flatmates were miraculously all in bed. Just in case of disturbance I locked the door and hung up my little notice. I didn't actually need it but I felt safer with it outside.

'I put the heater on even though it wasn't cold and curled up on my bed, warming the vibrator on my body. When I turned it on and heard the noise it made I went right under the bedclothes with it. It was so loud I thought it would wake up my flatmate.

'But she didn't arrive pounding at the door, so after a while, I managed to relax. I used the massage oil on my genitals to make them slippery and then I moved the vibrator up and down my labia like I would my fingers. After a while it felt so good on the clitoris that I concentrated there. I moved the vibrator ever so gently and lightly up and down the right side of my clitoris (that's where it felt best). And I had an orgasm; quite quickly. I *think* it was an orgasm.

'I got a few waves of nice feeling but they quickly finished. Then I remembered afterwards what you said about continuing the stimulation once the orgasm began which is what I didn't do. I put the vibrator back again when I remembered but it was too late. The excitement wouldn't come back.'

'How many times have you used the vibrator?' I ask.

'I tried it twice more', she replies. 'I did try keeping it on my clitoris longer each session but (I don't understand why) I seem to move off unconsciously when I reach climax.'

'You sound as though you're blocking it out,' says Kate. 'You're nearly there but you're a bit scared of what's going to happen so your mind sends a message to the hand holding the vibrator and says "Move off before we both blow up".'

'What should I do?' asks Maggie.

'Try and turn it into a YES/NO exercise. Tell yourself that if you're going to do it, there's no point unless you're prepared to give your body a decent chance. Insist upon staying with the stimulation when you get to the confusing, explosive bit,' I suggest.

Maggie's mother has arrived to stay with her daughter. 'We talked for a long time last night. We've never really talked like two adults before. My mother has never previously breathed a word about how she feels about Dad. I told her about my fear of confronting him and all of a sudden she began to open up.

'It came out with a rush, pent-up as if it's been bottled inside her for years. She finds him impossible, could never tell anyone because she thought she'd lose face. She's stuck it out all these years because of me. Now I'm not there she's asking herself what life is all about.

'I suggested she should leave him and her immediate reaction was panic. "What would I do?" she asked. "How would I live?" I suggested she ought to get some kind of retraining. "He'd never let me" she kept on saying. But I don't think that's true. I just don't think she's considered any alternative before.'

'How are you feeling about all this?' asks Mary.

'Pretty upset,' she says. 'It's awful to think about how unhappy she is. But I also feel sorry for my Dad too. The sad thing is he has no idea how awful he is to live with. He just thinks that's how things should be between man and wife.

'But I still think, even if it's going to be scary, that Mum ought to try and start a life independently from him. If she feels leaving him is too much, she could at least get a job that would take her out of the house and give her some money of her own. So tomorrow I'm going to ring up a Citizen's Advice Bureau and find out details of retraining schemes. It can't hurt.'

HALEY

Haley has not enjoyed her vibrator. 'I was getting on far better with my fingers and with Len's fingers. It seems a more natural pace. The first time we used the vibrator I thought it was going to run away with me. It was terrifying. The second time, instead of getting me excited, I went numb. I ended up being unable to respond at all. I had to give myself a break of about twenty minutes before I could masturbate with my fingers instead.'

VIBRATOR VERSUS FINGERS

Some women are more stimulated by finger manipulation than by electrically-generated vibration. Haley may be one of them but it would be a mistake to discard the vibrator on the strength of having used it only twice. Haley agrees to try it a few more times in the next week. She also decides to try the vibrator through a layer of soft material. Numbness can be the result of too strong a vibration on a super-sensitive clitoris.

JAN

Everyone in the group has written down their SHOULD/SHOULD NOT exercise and most people's resolutions are similar. Jan's list includes 'I should not eat chips', 'I should be more decisive', 'I should learn to live alone' and 'I should not be afraid to make the first move in finding a man'.

Jan is still hovering on the brink of whether or not actively to go out and look for another boy friend. Is it unfeminine to be so forward? Isn't that sort of behaviour unromantic?

Yes, debates the group, it is unfeminine in the old-fashioned sense of the word, but so what? Many men *like* to be actively pursued. It's not only a compliment to them but it takes some of the 'courting' responsibility off their shoulders. Why should it always be the men who are expected to make the running?

As for 'not being romantic', there are women aged eighty still sitting in the isolation of their family homes waiting for Mr Right to come along and sweep them off their feet. Much more fun to ring up Mr Right and ask him out. Saves about sixty years' waiting time. And such new found positiveness is the basis of all self-determination.

Jan and her vibrator have taken to each other. Jan has never found it difficult to masturbate to orgasm. Her climax pattern is to become excited quickly, to reach orgasm easily, then to have the excitement rapidly dwindle. Very occasionally she has climaxed twice in ten minutes but this is not something that happens often.

With her new electric friend she finds she can have rapid multiple orgasms. 'Just as one is over,' she explains, 'another begins about five or ten seconds later. The first is a long one, then there's this series of shorter but extremely intense climaxes. Then as the seconds go by there are greater and greater gaps of time between each orgasm. I almost have to force the last one out. I quite consciously arch my body up to the vibrator for it.'

'What's Jim's reaction?' asks Lucy.

'He doesn't know I'm using the vibrator,' says Jan. 'I've only tried it out during the day. Mind you, he's not been in too much lately to see me. He's been spending more and more time round at his new girl friend's place.'

'So it's not worth saying anything to him about it then?' continues Lucy.

'No, I don't think so. Even if he takes another six months to move out we don't have much left between us. Except Luke of course,' she adds wryly. 'At least Jim's been relatively quiet this week. Which means that Luke and I are beginning to feel a little less tense.'

'Are you going to ask him to go?' Haley is curious.

'I don't have to do anything as formal as that. We've shouted and screamed so much about busting up and him moving out that it's pretty well understood to be on the cards. I'm just sorry *I* can't move out to speed things up. But since it's my flat I've got to stick it out. But don't worry. He'll go. There's no way we can go on living like this. He may not go tomorrow but he'll go eventually.'

Anne says, 'You're sounding very decisive now. Are you quite sure you're doing the right thing?'

'I think I'd known we weren't going to work out for a long time. I was too scared to do anything active about it before. But since I joined the group I can see that there are alternatives. And though he still has the ability to reduce me to jelly I can harden up again afterwards. As long as I remember that, then I can cope.'

Lucy says, 'You've been coping for a long time already if you ask me. You'll find things a whole lot easier once you've got your place to yourself.'

MARY

Mary has had a hectic week of caring for her small children and getting ready to move house. Her contract with Bruce is still holding out and she is still feeling relief as a result of it.

'He's been working very hard this week,' she tells us. 'He comes home after a gruelling day at the office and launches into helping me, packing up our belongings and painting the new house. He's been great. What constantly amazes me though is that even when he's exhausted he still wants sex. I'm sure I must have a far lower libido than he has. But he's been very very nice this week and I've appreciated him. It's got nothing to do with sex, mind you.

'I think the new house is going to make a great difference. It's something for us to work on together which we both enjoy. We won't be so overcrowded, and it's got a garden which is going to be fantastic for the children. For the past two years I've had children and nappies and a dog squashed into a tiny house in an area I don't even like. I feel better just thinking about moving.'

One of Mary's SHOULDS is 'I should remember Bruce is tired in the evening, therefore I should do more housework myself instead of relying on him', and another is 'I should show Bruce more affection'. Her use of the vibrator has been desultory. 'I don't feel I need it,' she says flatly. 'I don't feel right using it. I did try. But only for a couple of minutes I admit. Mind you, having heard what you've just said to Maggie, I think I should give myself another go. A lot of my antagonism to it is due to prejudice. It's the same feeling I started off with about massage.'

KATE

Kate has been re-reading the Betty Dobson book *Liberating Masturbation*, and in particular has been looking at the drawings of female genitals. 'They are remarkable,' she says. 'She's made me feel a whole lot better about myself. I really thought my vulva was ugly and dirty, like a gaping wound. But now I begin to see the beauty, how flower-like a woman can look. I was pretty unhappy about using the speculum before, but I'm going to try again this week. I'm curious to have a better look at myself now.'

Kate *has* been using the vibrator, but although she has climaxed with it, she has developed certain fears.

VIBRATOR FEARS

'I've read that you can get hooked on a vibrator,' she says. 'Do you think that's true?'

If the alternative to being 'addicted' to a vibrator is to do without orgasms, I know which I'd plump for. I've heard of women who have been unable to masturbate by hand after getting to know and love a vibrator, whereas I know of others who are happy to respond both to manual and electric accompaniment. Jo, my assistant, first learnt to orgasm with a plain battery vibrator, subsequently learnt to do it with her fingers, and eventually managed it in bed with her lover without any sexual aids. On the other hand, some women get set in their masturbation patterns and if they have become fixated on using a vibrator, may find it difficult to climax without it. But it is possible to change the pattern in which you masturbate (just as it's possible to learn how to climax) which means it is possible to be weaned from a vibrator to other methods of satisfaction.

Even though you may depend mainly on a vibrator for sexual satisfaction, this does not mean you are limited to solitary, electric self-stimulation. It is very easy to take your vibrator to bed with a partner so that you both get fun and pleasure from it. Next week, we talk in detail about how to use the vibrator during lovemaking.

BISEXUALITY

Kate has been dying to ask Haley something for the last four weeks. Finally she plucks up her courage. 'I get turned on by thinking of other women,' she tells us. 'In the dreams I've had when I've woken up having an orgasm I've been watching a woman with very big breasts. I've often wondered if I might be bisexual.

'I feel very affectionate towards some of my girl friends. When I did that massage with my friends, it was lovely to be able to massage Suki as well as our men friends. I liked having the opportunity to touch a woman. But I do have fears that if I actually made love to another woman I'd never want to make love to a man again.

'What happened, Haley,' she asks, 'when you made love with a woman? How did you feel afterwards?'

Haley blushes. 'I met my friend socially, at a local party. We got on so well that we each knew we were attracted to the other. It was like a kind of mental shorthand between us. We didn't talk much about it, we were instantly very close.

I told Len how attracted I felt to her and he was very understanding. He told me that if I really wanted to get together with her, this was OK with him, he quite understood.

'Having virtually been given permission, I think my passion and my curiosity were strong enough to make me do something about her. I invited my friend over to our house for supper one evening. And we went to bed together. It seemed a perfectly natural thing to do.

'Going to bed was pretty successful too. It was very exciting and very sexy and I discovered myself having great insight into what turned men on. She enjoyed it, she could have orgasms very easily; I enjoyed it too, but couldn't let go sexually in the same way. But I loved being with her, and we met again a couple of times later and became great friends. Because I liked her didn't mean, though, that I lost all interest in men. I'm still very keen on Len. In fact I like him better for allowing me to do something I needed to do. I don't think I'm a very representative bisexual though. My main sexual friend is definitely Len. Jane has turned into a very close person, but the sexual curiosity has mostly died away. I think a real bisexual is some-one who likes the opposite sex just as much as they like their own sex.'

DR CHARLOTTE WOLFF

In her book *Bisexuality* (Quartet 1978) Dr Charlotte Wolff describes sexuality as a spectrum. At one end is the very heterosexual person sexually interested only in the opposite sex. A little further along the band is the person who very occasionally wants a relationship with some-one of the same sex but who usually prefers a heterosexual friendship. Then, in the middle of the spectrum is the person who is happy to have relationships equally with both men and women (a 50/50 bisexual). Next there is the person who occasionally has relationships with the opposite sex but more frequently with the same sex, and finally, on the other side of the spectrum is the person who prefers an exclusively homosexual relationship.

Everyone is 'constitutionally' bisexual but the quotient of bisexual behaviour can vary greatly. Haley's bisexuality sounds weighted heavily on the side of heterosexuality. Peggy, from an earlier group, had almost exclusively lesbian relationships but very occasional affairs with men. Jane, a married woman with a loving husband, also has two lovers: one is male, the other female. Susannah, on the other hand, has never married but has lived with several people. For five years she lived with a man, then she went through a phase of dating both men and women. Later she lived with a woman for three years and now has been with her male lover for the last two years.

Few of us actually use this natural capacity for loving both men and women. With the advent of feminism and a growing sense of 'sisterhood', it's become somewhat easier for women to explore friendships with other women. Women's liberation has opened a channel of bisexual or lesbian communications that was previously silted up. Men, however, are still much more armoured against ambiguous intimacies.

Kate was relieved to hear Haley had not apparently been overtaken by her desire for women to the extent of wanting to cut men out of her life.

'Nobody would force you to do that,' remonstrated Lucy. 'Nobody's going to make you do anything you don't really want to do.'

'You're right of course,' says Kate, pulling a face.

'What's so terrible about finding out you're a lesbian anyway?' asks Jan.

'There's so much social opposition to lesbians,' argues Kate. 'I'd be very scared if I found out that I were one.'

'But if you really *were* a lesbian,' says Jan, 'loving a woman would seem much better to you than loving a man.'

'That's true,' she agrees. 'But it still doesn't stop it from being scary.'

'Anyway, it's OK to love women as well as men,' says Haley. 'And if you don't want to go ahead and love women, nobody's forcing you. You're a free agent Kate.'

LUCY

Lucy remains quiet until the last woman has spoken. But she's been talking a lot more than usual today although she hasn't, so far, contributed anything new about herself. This week she seems different. In the past she's sat around, elegant but solemn. Today she's smiling and moving, more awake and alert in the group than ever before.

'I didn't have time for my vibrator all week,' she tells us. 'I didn't use it till last night. I flounced into my flat at the end of the day in a stinking bad mood, exhausted and irritable, dumped my bags in the living room and went to the loo.

'My loo is in the bathroom and the vibrator was sitting on one of the bathroom shelves. In a fit of bad temper I picked it up and thought, "Oh, what the hell. I might as well". And tried it. In three minutes flat I had the most amazing multiple orgasm, out of nowhere. It was fantastic.' She finishes with the air of a showman flourishing her arms.

Laughter and clapping come from the group. 'That's fantastic,' says Jan. 'Congratulations,' beam the others. 'Have you tried again?' asks Haley.

'Not yet,' replies Lucy, smiling. 'But I'm dying to get home tonight.'

In the second half of tonight's meeting we talk about the use of fantasy in our sex lives, and how menstruation may affect not only us and the way in which we react and feel, but how it can influence our husbands, children, partners and workmates.

FANTASY

Fantasy is still a relatively unexplored territory of our sexual lives for the obvious reasons that it's not the easiest subject to quantify. How do you measure imagination?

Despite this, social scientists in the past few years have been gathering information on the relationship between sexual fantasies and body stimulation. One such researcher, Dr Glenn Wilson of the London Institute of Psychology, has published a book on the subject, *The Secrets of Sexual Fantasy* (Dent). In it he presents a number of facts and figures.

His findings indicate that the amount we fantasise is related directly to the strength of the sex urge. But . . . if we have been conditioned against sexual feelings at some stage in our lives (as most of us have) the sex urge may be inhibited by feelings of guilt. And the feelings of guilt probably dampen down the fantasies. Certainly many of the women who have come to my groups have not previously had sexual fantasies.

So, just because you've never had fantasies, it doesn't necessarily mean you have a low libido. Nor does this mean you are unable to develop both the ability to fantasise and the ability to experience sexual climax. For there have now been several documented cases of women taught to become orgasmic by first of all turning on to erotic pictures or films, and second, by being encouraged to turn on to the memory of them. So it *is* possible to develop our sexuality through expanding the imagination. Interestingly, the converse also appears to be true; hand in hand with self-knowledge about the body's erotic responses goes a growth of the erotic imagination.

HILARY

'I started off fantasising as a teenager and I suppose then my fantasies were based on reality. I would see a bloke in the street, fancy him and wonder what it would be like to go to bed with him. I would find myself picturing myself having sex with him. I think the proximity of the man had a lot to do with how I got turned on. I could do this with people I was talking to, standing close to. I would suddenly find I was off in a sexual day dream about him even while he stood there chatting in front of me. And I would have an orgasm. I didn't know it was an orgasm at the time. But I'd get waves of lovely feelings and a lot of tingly sensations. I'm sure now, looking back, that they were orgasms and not just excitement.

Much later, when I was about twenty-three, I would orgasm during sex only if I was crazily in love. I felt these orgasms very much in my vagina. I was never aware of my clitoris being touched or even being involved with the sensations. It was very much to do with copulation. But I *had* to be madly in love. The less intense I felt, the less good were the feelings.

I'd never really masturbated. I mean, I had when I was about thirteen with another girl. But that was just playing around. When we found a good spot, we thought, that's nice, so we hung around those good sensations. But I didn't know that we were masturbating. And I never, ever did it with myself.

When I started going to bed with men regularly, at about eighteen, I think I was as much in love with the art of sex as with sex itself. I used to think about it for three hours beforehand and build up to it in every way. I'd go through a whole ritual of rigorous perfuming and talcing. Every inch of me, every orifice would smell good and look good. In fact, looking good was a great part of it. If I knew I looked spotty and horrid, it wouldn't work. If I don't turn myself on I'm not capable of turning anyone else on.

'I think all this preparation had a lot to do with insecurity too. I was very unconfident then. Had to build up my own ego to go into the fray. But also the ritual of the preparation was a kind of fantasy for me. It would work me up and make me sexy.

'With Gordon I was in love for the first time in an adult way. I couldn't wait to leap into bed with him. And when I got there we were immediately very sexual. There didn't have to be such a great build-up. For the first time I had specific waves of orgasmic feeling, great waves of it. Really marvellous. I didn't fantasise with him at all. I was twenty-three then.

'I often couldn't see him for a very long time. And I missed him very much. I was married but I simply couldn't get tuned into my husband's lovemaking at all. He was far too aggressive and matter-of-fact about it. I'd lie awake for hours beside him in bed, missing Gordon violently. And that's when I first began truly to fantasise. Without moving a muscle (I couldn't, for fear of waking up Hugh, it was like being in prison) I'd remember all the very sexy incidents of my lovemaking with Gordon, and I'd come. Without touching myself or moving any part of me, I'd have a climax. Those orgasms started right in the brain. Hot liquid feeling would shoot down me, I'd be very moist between the legs, and feel very hot on the outer lips, waves of lovely feeling would go through me. I'd feel it most in the stomach and the vagina. It would be as though the mental action of my fantasy would get taken over by the physical action of my body.

'I didn't do this only in bed, either. I used to do it, quite involuntarily, standing in a bus queue.

'At the time when Parker was my lover (I was twenty-six) I really got into sexy underwear. I became turned on by wearing lacy black pants and frilly suspender belts, so much so that I started to wear them in bed. And from then on it just seemed a natural addition to put a bit of rope here and there, tie each other to the bedposts, mostly me being tied, I must say. We were acting out roles that I guess were coming out of our heads from somewhere. Perhaps they were fantasies that had always been there.

'Then a couple of years later with Adrian I went through a period of straight but very exciting sex. We did a lot of screwing in cars, and since the whole relationship was illicit, it was very exciting anyway.

'Eventually we spent a week together in a flat in Brighton. That was some week. Where Parker had been reluctant to do anything to me that might even remotely hurt, Adrian was far more dominant and explorative.

'We were both into constraint. He once tied me up with my stockings. I'd do wild, sexy strips for him, taking off, very slowly, my sexiest, flimsiest underwear. I'd perform for him in the sleaziest strip club way. My love life was absolutely great for a while.

'Eventually I left Hugh for Adrian and I had a more regular relationship, less an affair, more of an open understanding. Then, suddenly I went off all this completely. I just didn't want to do it. I think I'd worked it out of my system. Which was pretty grim for Adrian. Because he'd bargained on having this ultra-sexy fetishistic girl, which had suited him perfectly. And there I was, changed.

'But to give Adrian credit, he's always been very innovative with sex, and I think he's been great for me. We somehow got back to screwing, but now, instead of me constantly performing for him, and us doing all these crazy things, he started telling me fantasies.

'He'd start by telling a story about something sexual, and the something sexual would be happening to me. Once I'd started to get turned on by it he would penetrate me and start fucking but would still carry on with the story at the same time. He's got a great imagination. He's an actor and a playwright and a lovely storyteller.'

Hilary is aware that her fantasies grow and expand out of each other. She isn't remotely bothered about the fact that in some of her fantasies she is abused, used and masturbated by men she finds gross and unattractive. She wants to feel like this *in her dream life*. In reality though, she's a strong, forceful character who has actively re-shaped her life and is someone who, if truly used and abused, would react strongly with defiance, disdain and dislike.

'Until I met Adrian, my fantasies were always rooted in reality. It was he who made me realise there is a world of sexy stories in my head.

'Then I discovered the vibrator and long-life batteries. I had used a vibrator a couple of times before. But it hadn't dawned on me to use it on the clitoris. I'd just put it in the vagina. I'd become turned on by it, but certainly not orgasmic.

'Once again things started off with Adrian taking the initiative and using the vibrator on me. Before rediscovering the vibrator I had always thought that my orgasms depended on how I felt at the time and who the person was. Now I know that's wrong.

'My vibrator fantasies are very different from the scenes with Adrian.

One of them is about me making a blue movie. There are a lot of people involved in this film, all watching from shadowy corners around the set. It starts with my making a deal, fixing the price, going into the business details.

'We start the movie. And once I get really excited I'll do anything. I'm out of control, not in command of my actions any more. And the film men can see that I'll do anything, and they start making suggestions, more and more outrageous suggestions, and each time, the crazier the things are the more excited I become. Until I come.

'I don't think I'd actually act out any of my fantasies. I've often wondered how I'd feel if I did. Would I get as turned on in real life? I'm sure I wouldn't. I do know that from being a teenager who thought she was frigid and never came, I've learnt through using the vibrator and my imagination that I'm highly sexed. I have two or three orgasms a day. Which is incredible when I think of the years of marriage where I remained sexually dead.'

Often, once the novelty of successful masturbation has worn off, it gets harder again to climax. This is often where the value of fantasy comes in. Because if you can learn to use fantasy either by thinking up your own or, failing a fertile imagination, by reading about somebody else's, you can spur yourself on to an easier climax.

SURE-FIRE FANTASIES

Very often the women in my classes haven't considered fantasising before and don't know where to start. Sadly there are very few good books of women's fantasies available. The best is Nancy Friday's *My Secret Garden* (Quartet/Futura). I have asked a few past members of the pre-orgasmic workshop to let me have what are sure-fire fantasies for them, the erotic scenes that arouse them while they are masturbating or making love. Perhaps they and the fantasies in *My Secret Garden* will be useful for women who want to know where to begin.

KATE (on whom the character of Kate in this book is partly based)
'I'd like to write my fantasies in three stages because I think it's very interesting how they changed as a result of coming to the workshop.
STAGE 1: 'Before coming to the pre-orgasmic workshop, I only experienced orgasm as the result of a dream, and I would come in the night as a result of the following fantasy. Always a woman appeared, sometimes standing behind a window. I would look in, she would take her clothes off, and on seeing her breasts, I would wake and come to orgasm.
STAGE 2: 'Since starting the workshop I have stopped coming in this way – no more dreams of women, and no more waking up having orgasms, with one exception: during the first part of the course I

became very conscious of the way I was allowing my boy friend and people at work to dominate me. I told my boy friend (and more important, acted on it) that either he decided we get together, or we quit. I then had a dream in which I was facing the problem of telling a colleague at work (I was her "senior") that she could not have her holiday at the time she wanted it. (This was a real problem in my life.) She began to complain. I then physically experienced a very powerful contraction in the vagina and woke up with orgasms! The next day, effortlessly, I told my colleague what the situation was on this issue.

STAGE 3: 'In conscious, waking life I can now fantasise, and with the help of a vibrator in such a way that it brings me to orgasm.

'In my fantasy I'm in the changing room at the squash club, Suki comes in, my boy friend Rupert's ex-girl friend. We are close friends in real life. She begins to undress – she's very bosomy – and another friend of mine, Mike, comes in too. He's tall, dark with thick curly hair. He is exposing himself, showing a large erection. I then come to orgasm.

'A slight development of the above, in Mike's sitting room where he's entertaining Suki and I. I get up and encourage Suki to kneel in front of Mike who's sitting on the sofa. Standing behind Suki I take off her jumper slowly still looking at Mike – he's transfixed by both of us. Slowly I begin to caress Suki. Mike begins to undress. He has an enormous erection, and I come immediately to orgasm.'

VIVIAN (from *My Secret Garden* by Nancy Friday)

I had this fantasy the very first time I had sex. Jimmy was the first man for me. He's still the only one, but no matter who I sleep with later on, I think I'll always have these thoughts I have with Jimmy. They just seem to automatically spring to mind whenever I open my legs.

Anyway, that first night, I don't think we slept very much . . . Maybe the second or third time that night, he put me into this position; I think it's the position that inspired this idea in the first place, the idea that I was being planted. I was lying on my back, all my weight on my shoulders, with my legs straight up and over his shoulders. He was high above me – I remember looking up and seeing him looming large over me and coming down into me, boring down on me. Straight *down* into me. Not a frightening picture – on the contrary, I felt very large and accommodating, very wide and open, waiting for him to fill me up with his thrust. Waiting for him to plant seed like I was a large, warm, fertile hole in the earth, there just for him, just for that purpose, to be planted. I was the earth and I was the hole in the earth. In fact, I was all hole, and he, he was like some great International Harvester Seed Planter moving down the field, me, moving from hole to hole with each thrust. And I was all the holes, I was the earth. I was planted again and again. It was so exciting . . . to be planted by an earth planting machine, his enormous International Harvester that could plunge deeper into the earth than anything, could fill me up and leave me planted, ripe . . . that was it, I suppose: not just the excitement of being planted, but of knowing that with each thrust I would be left whole, complete. Can you understand that? It wasn't the machine that was exciting – though the inexorable size of it was. What was exciting was the seed part. Or me being the earth. God, I don't know . . . but I love that feeling.

LINDA
'I'm not too hot on fantasies. It may be that I'm not sufficiently imaginative. My major one is swimming in clear blue water (sea – not lakes) under a brilliant sky. My husband and I attempted lovemaking in just such a situation once; maybe it was because there was no tension, because expectations of success were so low, that I now see it as the ideal.

'A friend of mine dreams of being stroked with oil, grease, anything slimy, and she does say that it helps her reach orgasm if her boy friend smothers her in grease beforehand.

'It also helps me just to think about the orgasmic experiences – to imagine what I will feel during orgasm and to imagine myself being made love to. But could that be classified as a projection rather than a fantasy?'

BETTY ANN
Betty Ann has always wanted to be an actress and dabbles in amateur theatricals, but she is too shy to actually audition for a role. She is unmarried and currently living with an aspiring young actor who is 'just a good friend'.

'My main problem is that I never have quite enough courage to do the things I really want to do. Same with men – I never go after the ones who really turn me on; instead, I stick with men who are harmless and devoted. But my fantasies are another story! My favourite fantasy scenario I call The Audition, and I think of it whenever I want to turn myself on.

'In it, I am an all-powerful figure – bold, arrogant, slightly cruel, and hard to please. It begins with dozens of men being sent up to audition for me. I am reclining on a couch, languidly watching them go through their paces. The purpose? To see who will have the immense good fortune to be my bed partner that night! A male secretary waits in the wings to usher in each new candidate. I dismiss one after another with a curt "Next!"

'Finally, in comes an adorable – and very nervous – creature. I let him wait while I jot down a few brief impressions. This gorgeous man is dressed in very tight bleached-out blue jeans and a soft white shirt unbuttoned a little so I can see the caramel-smooth skin of his chest. He has tiny hips and a lovely, small bottom outlined perfectly by the thin material of his jeans. I ask him to turn around, appreciating the play of muscles in his ropy thighs as he pivots slowly, and then to recite his vital statistics, including the size of his penis.

'This makes him blush, but I am very businesslike. I order him to strip slowly. By the time he's down to his tiny white briefs, I have to admit he's perfect. As he's beginning to peel them down, I call out sharply: 'I want you to lower them very slowly. Try to excite me – *think* about what you're doing.''

'He tucks his thumbs in the briefs, inclining his pelvis slightly – rocking it in slight, undulating movements – and teasing the material down a millimeter at a time.

'First I get a glimpse of his curly, blond pubic hair, and then a tantalising view of the beginnings of his prick. He slips his hands down and allows his strong, tapering fingers to caress the outer edges of his tense thighs, making cupping motions to emphasise and frame the swelling bulge.

'"Nice, very nice," I say professionally. "Before you show me what you've got, tell me what you'll do to me if you're chosen."

'Stammering, he tells me how much he wants to make love to me, to lick me from my toes to the nape of my neck.

'Finally, he pulls the briefs all the way down and his penis catapults out, fully erect and straining out towards me, rock-hard and sort of . . . pleading. I can see a pulse beating in his groin as he stands before me; a small groan escapes his lips and it looks to me as if his knees will buckle if I don't do something quick.

'"All right," I say briskly. "You've been selected. Be back at nine o'clock tonight." Then he's taken off to a recovery room until his erection subsides.

'In this scenario, I remain cool and collected, but the *real* me – the one imagining all this – is almost at the brink of climax just fantasising about it . . .'

Since fantasies are like dreams they cannot really be resisted although I have shown that they can be encouraged. Any woman can find herself, despite herself, thinking about erotic situations at any moment in her life. She can try and forget this. But why should she? Sexual fantasies are not 'policeable': they can't be 'correct' or 'incorrect', because they are not real. Fantasies can represent doubts, fears, suppressions of ourselves as often as they represent any aspect of our true, conscious selves. People can be aroused by imaginary behaviour which in their waking lives they would completely reject. Why this is so is complicated and not really fully understood. But fantasies may be extended and enjoyed simply for their pleasurable by-product – enhancing both your own sex life and, through *your* enjoyment, hopefully your partner's too. Just as it would be illogical to feel guilty about your dreams, it is also illogical to feel as though you are 'cheating' on your partner by thinking of another situation or person during lovemaking. Successful sex in a relationship contains a selfish element, as we discussed in Chapter 1. Nobody else can have your orgasm for you. That is a private moment in your own consciousness. Similarly, lovemaking means surrendering to sex itself, including sexual thoughts, as well as accepting and initiating the embraces of a lover.

MENSTRUAL CYCLE

Not only are there phases in our lives when we find it hard to turn on, due to past inhibitions and present guilt feelings, but in addition, being women, we can be subject to a constant monthly turmoil of emotions. For along with the monthly menstrual *body* cycle, goes a monthly *emotional* cycle. Many women experience a peak of sexual desire at and around menstruation and many experience another peak around the time of ovulation (roughly the middle of each cycle).

Of course there have been many taboos in the past against having sexual relations at the time of menstruation, based on religous beliefs and practices. Women have therefore been taught to think of themselves as repellent at the time of their flow of blood (literally unclean). Not unnaturally, any sexual feelings on their part at such times have often been repressed.

If, however, instead of marking off the 'monthlies' as a no-sex time, we do the opposite and begin to develop them as a best-sex time, some delightful and sensual experiences may be the result. For this is not only a phase of increased body-sensitivity but also an emotional peak. Of course, it *is* also a period of clumsiness and sometimes increased accident-proneness, but in the past it has only been these negative qualities that were dwelt on. It may be of far-reaching importance to understand that the time around menstruation (the *paramenstrum*) can be the most creative, sensitive and sensual passage of the month.

Authors Peter Redgrove and Penelope Shuttle who have published the first English book on the psychology of menstruation (*The Wise Wound*, Gollancz Ltd 1978) encourage women to document their own cycles by keeping a menstruation diary.

HOW TO KEEP A MENSTRUATION DIARY

Record daily, your moods, physical feelings (whether you are tired, energetic, feel sexy, feel ill) your dreams, fantasies, body changes, and sexual activity. By doing this, not by the calendar month but by the menstrual month, it is possible to draw a chart of where to expect your moods and activities to lie on future days of the month.

I tried it out myself as an experiment. Here I reproduce some excerpts from my diary.

PARAMENSTRUM: Thursday 5 January. Day 24 Feel as though face is bloated because my eyes are trying hard to see from underneath puffed-out eyebrows. My mood in the morning is sleepy and I remember vaguely dreaming something complicated about sex therapy in the office. In the afternoon, after a day's hard work, I find myself becoming rapidly enraged, and hostile, focused on one particular member of the staff, who is being particularly offensive. I'm aware however that my symptoms are extremely pre-menstrual. Nevertheless I am in such a rage on my way home that I reach a crisis point. Having done that, I float free of the anger and start being constructive with the thoughts and feelings about work. I go through alternate rages and moments of calm, setting my life to rights for an hour and a half. And by eleven o'clock although I still have the puffy-eyes feeling and know I'm tired, I've done a good day's work. Totally unsexual, I go to bed, and fall asleep over my book.

Friday 6 January. Day 25 Am woken by a phone call. Am instantly awake and charming to friend. On putting down phone am extremely loving and cuddly with rather closer friend. In sharp contrast to yesterday, this morning I'm relaxed, clear eyed, fresh, feeling like work, feeling alive, and I'm sensual. Can't tear myself away from lovely man. Could quite happily stay stroking and cuddling him all day long. Feelings of joie de vivre and sensuality remain all day. While I'm typing this, shortly after work, I'm wondering how I can lure my man into bed. He's been talking about needing exercise and going for a run. Perhaps, instead, if I casually wandered into the kitchen . . . ? So much energy whirring inside me.

Saturday 7 January. Day 26 and, as it turns out, Day 1 We made love last night, not on my part from a compulsive need to do it, but because we sort of drifted into it. In fact, to begin with I wasn't even sure if I wanted to. But once we'd begun, I was very glad because I was in one of those marvellous physical states where all my sensations were velvet,. Anywhere I was touched, and any touch I put out to him, felt floating and exquisite. Each bit of my flesh was full of tiny air bubbles, all receiving stroking delight. I didn't orgasm in the end, because it would have taken too long. I really could have stayed being stroked and touched all night. It was marvellous.

Discovered in the morning why I'd felt so sensual. My period began, two days early. If someone could market whatever it is that floats through my body the night before a period, they'd be the world's greatest millionaire.

Still slightly tetchy, but not very much. And it alternates with great feelings of caring for Phillip. Perhaps if we could make love all day throughout the days immediately at the beginning of a period I'd do away with all pre-menstrual snappiness.

The blood speeds up through the day, until in the evening it's flowing fast. I'm very tired by night time but find it hard to sleep, my body doesn't feel really comfortable, and Phillip's movements wake me up once or twice.

Sunday 8 January. Day 2 Body is tired but I'm using my early morning energy to work. This afternoon I'll flake out. Blood flowing fast still and I'm a little achey. I do have a desire this weekend for walking. Did a lot of it yesterday, and would like to again this afternoon. I don't normally get this urge. I don't feel particularly sensual today though I suspect that's because such a great part of me wants to work. Which cuts out the time I actually want to spend in bed. Later, later . . .

In fact, not at all. Come bedtime I was totally off sex, to the point of feeling thoroughly fed up when he wanted to make love. The sweet thing was I discovered, halfway through, that he was only doing it for me. We gave up. Thoroughly exhausted. Got a bit tearful again but it didn't last. Not like yesterday night which I forgot to mention, but for some reason I cried my head off.

LEADING UP TO OVULATION TIME: Tuesday 17 January. Day 11 I'm exhausted all day from my paltry sleep and fall into bed, demanding and receiving a reading from *Martin Chuzzlewit* which does a lot to make me feel better about Phillip. I sleep, although he wakes in a sweat every two hours.

Wednesday 18 January. Day 12 In the morning we give away the remains of our frozen Cornish catch (last night's indigestible fish) to a friend. I make a point of saying don't wake me up when you come to bed, aware that Phillip is going to do his turning up at two in the morning routine, after reading in the bath. I'm defiant about my sleep and desperately tired. I felt totally unrandy last night, although I suspect he was sexy. I wonder if it's the mind turning the body off on purpose, because I woke in the night and sleepily masturbated.

Sunday 22 January. Day 16 I'm awakened at nine o'clock this morning by my dreams.

OVULATION TIME? Monday 23 January. Day 17 My discharge changes to brownish-red stain. Does this mean I'm ovulating now? I'm certainly dreaming a lot. I woke this morning with fragments of three dreams rushing through my head, concerning my workshops and the people I meet at work.

Phillip points out that it's the full moon tonight. Perhaps that is the cause, he suggests, of my restlessness and generally nasty mood today. It certainly has been a bad, jerky sort of a day. I've been out of sorts, wanting to burst into tears, unable to cope with being hassled at work and overcome by an engulfing sub-editing job. Totally sexless in addition.

Tuesday 24 January. Day 18 I'm not much better today. I'm a bit jollier but very tired. I *do* manage to relax with the kids in the afternoon, but for the rest of the day, I'm on edge. P. says it's because I haven't had any sex. He could be right, but I refuse him again tonight.

Wednesday 25 January. Day 19 Calming down somewhat although I'm *still* tired, but then I have been slaving over my office work and it's been draining me.

Thursday 26 January. Day 20 I have a manic energy which whisks me through a very busy day. I am, needless to say, when I crawl into bed, dog tired. My climax turns out to be frighteningly strong tonight. It's so strong that momentarily I block it off, cutting out the feelings. But then I force myself to unblock and let that incredible vibrant strength shake my whole body and I scream as loudly as I can. Thank heavens Bobby's no longer in the next room. And it's very scary. P. too is pretty rampant, and comes strongly himself. Of course, none of this force is surprising since this is the fifth day since we've fucked, and speaking for myself, I've only masturbated once in that time. Obviously one's sex energy stores up as in a generator and is only released when it's used.

In the past months, through continuing this kind of detailed self-monitoring, I've discovered that, regular as clockwork, I begin a heavy stringy discharge on Day 12. Around Day 16 or 17 I become exhausted for exactly 48 hours, meantime experiencing a slightly discoloured discharge possibly tinged with blood. During this fatigue I sleep uncomfortably and dream incessantly. (I assume I am ovulating.) As I reach Day 25 and onwards I'm tetchy and irritable but I'm beginning to feel sexier. The night before my period is sexual magic and I'm drumming with creative energy. From Day 1 to Day 12 I'm sexy. Then, once again, with the onset of the Day 12 discharge, my easy sexuality switches off like a time clock. Which has put my ego in its place because I honestly thought of myself, previously, as being sexy all the time. Whereas, instead, rather too often I'm irritable, moody, and unsensual.

DIFFERING LIBIDOS

One of the reasons women come to pre-orgasmic workshops is because their husbands/partners are objecting to their lack of interest in sex. Of course, if there is a marriage of a person of high libido to a person of low libido there are going to be discrepancies. For although both partners are 'normal' they won't match up.

The general solution is a compromise. One partner is going to have to make love rather more often than feels natural while the other must be prepared to cool things and make a lot more use of self-stimulation. If everything else in the partnership is good, this is the best way to keep the sexual peace.

Every monthly cycle varies. Although for about two-thirds of *my* cycle I don't feel very sexy, I am capable of having an orgasm providing the stimulation *is stepped up*. But it becomes much harder than in the lovely sensitive days of Day 1 to 12. Anorgasmic women, eighteen per cent of women, according to the sample in *The Hite Report* by Shere Hite, are in a permanent state of 'not feeling sexy'. What they don't know, because they have *never* found it easy to climax, is that they are probably capable of it, providing they persevere and providing they *increase the stimulation*.

Thus, not only may a particular woman's libido differ to her mate's but, in addition, it can differ in itself from week to week. What is the answer? Is it 'natural' and 'right' to accept that you are unlikely to climax? Or is it advisable to change what some describe as 'natural'?

Since I know it's in *my nature* to enjoy some delightful lovemaking during the 'unsexy' days, and, with a little perserverence, to experience some poignant orgasms, I would think it is more than OK to bring about a change. Happily, nothing appalling has happened to my health after twenty years of an active sex life.

So, to those women who've not yet enjoyed a climax and to others who think they have a low libido, the message reads *you can intensify your sexuality if you want to*. And one of the easiest ways to do that is by making use of a vibrator, or a fantasy.

ADDITIONAL READING

The Secrets of Sexual Fantasy by Dr Glenn Wilson (Dent)
My Secret Garden by Nancy Friday (Quartet/Futura)
The Wise Wound by Penelope Shuttle and Peter Redgrove (Gollancz) now out of print but probably available from a library.

WEEK FIVE HOMEWORK DAILY SCHEDULE

One hour a day.
Repeat breathing, bio-energetics and Kegels every day.

Do bath/self-massage when you can and then go on to masturbation work. If you want to pursue the self-stimulation by hand, give yourself at least thirty minutes on it. If you get bored or fed up, take a short break and then carry on. (It takes many women up to an hour of continuous stimulation to reach orgasm at first.)

If you feel you are getting nowhere with the manual masturbation, experiment with the vibrator. How do you feel about using it? If last week you have already used the vibrator, continue noticing the pattern of your sexual response, noting down any queries to discuss in the group.

CHAPTER 6
Week six

Week Six is a celebration and a farewell. Jo's tabby cat winds his way among the glasses on the floor. We're having a festive drink to say goodbye.

Although it's finishing off time for the group, Kate, Haley, Lucy and Jan are already making plans to continue meeting. Before we get down to our goodbye massage, though, there are a few pleas for help. Unprecedentedly, Lucy speaks first.

LUCY

'I've been so thrilled with the vibrator,' she tells us, 'that I've tried it every night. And it's getting harder and harder to come. It was lovely to begin with but on the third night I took much longer to get excited. On the fourth and fifth night it either took hours and then the climax didn't feel very good or I gave up altogether. Why? What's happened?'

'Sounds as though your body is working out its natural sexual pace,' I venture. 'Maybe you're not someone who needs immense multiple orgasms every night. Maybe, if you only used the vibrator every third night, you'd leave your body enough time to re-charge its sexual batteries.

'On the other hand, it may be that you are beginning to get used to the vibrator and that once it's no longer a novelty you need an added stimulus.'

'Such as fantasy?' suggests Kate, who had used it a little herself.

'Or possibly a bit of both,' says Lucy to herself. 'Did anyone else find this happened?'

MAGGIE

Maggie shakes her dark head in an emphatic cloud of no. 'I tried building up the excitement and then stopping, then beginning again.

And I gave myself hours. When I did finally get to a strong peak of excitement I carried on with the vibration and held the feeling right there. I didn't take the vibrator off this time and although it felt very weird and confused I did come. It wasn't at all what I expected. I've been expecting this cascade of marvellous feeling. And instead, it was just like a motor turning over a few times before it died again. It was OK, but I found it disappointing. I thought it would be much better than it was.'

'But you've done marvellously,' cries Haley. 'Last week you couldn't even let yourself stay with the vibration. That's fantastic. This week you've actually allowed yourself to go over into an orgasm. That's wonderful progress.'

'I expect you simply need to practise,' says Jan. 'It sounds as though you're being very tentative over letting yourself come. At least you've begun. When you get used to the sensations, you'll probably let yourself go a little more each time. And when you do, your orgasm will come out a bit stronger each time.'

'Try and open yourself up to the sensation,' suggests Haley. 'Try and abandon yourself to the feelings, instead of trying to fight them. Throw yourself into the jumble and confusion. I know it can be a bit frightening, but nothing terrible will happen to you.'

'I am scared of losing consciousness,' Maggie admits. 'That's what I feel might happen. I'm frightened of actually passing out. I've read that some women do.'

'Some men do too,' says Mary. 'My husband did the very first time he had sex with anyone when he was nineteen.'

'It's a fear of losing control, isn't it?' I contribute. 'But as we've said earlier, (Chapter 4) when you climax you do momentarily lose control and move into a different consciousness while you're actually in the throes of orgasm. A very few people occasionally do faint but that tends only to be when they are at an extreme of excitement. It is very unlikely that you will lose complete consciousness, Maggie. But you will be focused inwards to the exclusion of what's going on around you. Doesn't mean to say you will faint, though.'

'It's getting over that fear that's going to help, isn't it,' Maggie muses.

'If you carry on using the vibrator and getting familiar with it, you'll probably find the fear goes away of its own accord.'

'What happened with your mother?' asks Jan.

Maggie brightens up. 'She went back to Dad yesterday. She doesn't really want to leave him, in spite of everything. But she's got inspired with enthusiasm for actually going out and doing something. We did investigate some of the retraining schemes but in the end she got very interested in going back into education. She thought doing something like a degree at the Open University would fit in with her life, at the same time giving her an opportunity to slowly start meeting new people and doing new things. Much better than the shock of being plunged into something completely new like a job or a full-time course. She's been at home for twenty-seven years. It's a very long time. It must be very frightening for her to begin something new. The Open University will ease her in gradually. She looked much happier when she went back, simply from having thought of an alternative to the miserable life she's been leading so far.'

She paused for an instant, looked a little shy and then spoke again. 'I made a decision too. I decided that if at the end of next summer I didn't have a better job or a boy friend, that I would go out to India where my boy friend is, providing of course that he still wants me to go out.'

'I thought you didn't want to go out there,' puzzled Mary.

'I didn't want to two years ago,' Maggie admits. 'But I feel now I'd like to see a country other than my own. I'll be scared by the travelling but I'll also be very interested in it.

'The other reason I didn't go two years ago was I didn't really think Joe wanted me. He was scared he would become totally responsible for me, trapped into marriage if you like. And now, I think I could go over, look after myself and if it didn't work out between him and me, I know I'm capable of getting back on my own. I feel a lot more confident than I did before. If he's willing to take the risk of having me over there, then I'm willing to take the risk of going.'

MARY

Having tried the vibrator again Mary has decided she prefers being aroused, by herself or her husband, using fingers.

'I suppose because we're in the throes of moving we've reached a stage in our lives where we're re-evaluating everything. Partly because I can actually come now, but mostly because we don't have to make love so often, our love life is getting much better. We had a long talk the other night. We resolved that with our move we are going to make our lives freer. Once we're settled in to the house we're going to give each other a lot more time off. We'll arrange it so that each can spend time separately from the other, nights away even, and that's going to be OK. It means we can have other lovers if we choose and it'll be acceptable to both of us.

'Sounds great, doesn't it! Whether or not it'll work I've no idea. But the way Bruce talked about it, I think he can cope with it, and I'm sure I can.'

'Aren't you afraid that one of you will fall in love with someone else?' asks Haley, appalled. 'Suppose that happens?'

'If that does happen we'll have to cope with it when it arrives. I don't think it will though, because he's so potty about me, and I think he's a great husband and a great friend. I know my pattern with lovers now and even if I do fall in love, the love fades away after a time.

'Bruce is a great husband for me. I value him very much, I value him particularly for coming to this kind of an agreement with me. There can't be many men who would do that. It would be very, very hard for me to meet up with someone who is going to be better than Bruce as a long-term prospect. And there's no point in my suddenly changing my life for any lover. I know that the odds are I'd lose interest in him after a few months. It just seems to be my pattern.'

'Rather you than me, friend,' says Jan. 'I find it hard enough concentrating on one person let alone two. Aren't you going to find your life terribly split up?'

Mary ponders this. 'I've never found the slightest problem with that when I've been having affairs before. The only difference now is that I'm going to be able to be open about them instead of deceitful.

'Look, if in time the arrangement turns out to be an awful mistake, we'll re-think it. We've discussed all this and we have gone into the problems. We're both more confident people now and therefore I think much more able to carry it off.'

JAN

'I'm sitting on totally the other side of the fence,' says Jan. 'All I want to do is settle down with the man of my dreams and live happily ever after. Meanwhile the man of my nightmares is still living in my flat, muttering dire threats of retribution. I thought he'd gone last week because a lot of his stuff disappeared but he returned a day later. I'm feeling surprisingly OK about him, mostly because I'm having such an amazing time with my vibrator. It doesn't have rows with me and it's such an accurate lover.'

'We've thought up a lovely lonely hearts ad for Jan,' Lucy tells us. 'The minute Jim finally gets out, she's sending it off. We spent last night egging each other on and getting up enough dutch courage to write it.'

'All I've got to do now,' says Jan 'is hope that someone nice will answer. I actually took the plunge this morning and posted the ad to the local newspaper.'

We all giggle and speculate on who might respond to it.

HALEY

'I tried using the vibrator through a silk scarf,' she tells us, 'to see if it felt any better. It did. I came and it was quite nice, but I really prefer using my fingers. It's something both Len and I have got good at now, and I associate it with being sexy. Somehow fingers turn me on much more. So we've decided to stick with them for the time being and just use the vibrator occasionally. There's nothing specially new to report. Len and I are getting on very well. He's delighted by the masturbation and I'm feeling particularly happy with him.'

KATE

'I've had mild orgasms with my vibrator,' she tells us. 'It doesn't seem to be so effective as before somehow. I've been using it with some of Ian's magazines which turn me on a lot. But it is getting harder to come.'

'This sounds like the time for a reminder,' I say. 'The batteries run down very rapidly in battery-operated vibrators. You must remember to change them often.'

Jan giggles. 'The man in charge of my electrical shop can't understand what I keep buying these batteries for. He's started asking me. It's getting quite difficult to explain.'

'Ever heard of bulk buying,' says Haley. 'That would solve the problem.'

'The vibrator slows down when the batteries are low,' I continue. 'And the slower it gets, the harder it is for you to achieve orgasm.'

'How are things with Ian?' Haley asks Kate.

'Not so good. He finds it very hard to accept my attempts at independence. He won't listen to the theory behind them. And he's shown no interest in the vibrator at all. I've wanted him to use it with me but he's been very heavy-handed and I can see that he's bored silly. None of which is particularly aphrodisiac. And he sends me into a towering rage which doesn't help things at all.'

Kate's problem with Ian is a natural lead-in to the second half of our discussion on the subject of how to combine vibrators with lovemaking.

MAKING LOVE TOGETHER

Hopefully, by Week Six, most members of the pre-orgasmic group have learnt how to make love to themselves. They will know by now which strokes of the fingertips and which vibratory pressures can turn them on *enough* to give them an orgasm.

Once this is the case, the next step, for those women who want to, is to bring this new-found knowledge into their relationships. The first move is to get the message across to the friend that by learning to masturbate his/her partner he/she can give maximum sensual pleasure. It's a good idea to give up sexual intercourse entirely and concentrate only on learning to bring each other to climax by hand.

It's what most teenagers used to do in the good old days when petting was OK but intercourse was not. (Days of courting are sometimes constructive since they give lovers opportunities to get to know each other more gradually physically.)

HOW TO HELP YOUR LOVER

The greatest difficulty here is not just that your partner may be 'doing it wrong' but in getting him/her to understand how 'to do it right'. It is of course desperately hard to give sex instructions when you are fearful; your partner will be discouraged by them and you may be worried that as a result he/she will eventually reject them and you. This is where the assertion exercises prove vital. You have everything to lose by not being brave enough to persist with your explanations and instructions, and nothing to gain if you are chicken and keep quiet.

If your partner really cares about you, he/she wants to hear your preferences, wants to learn, and above all is motivated by longing to give *you* pleasure.

There are ways of getting practical information across without mortally wounding your friend. One of the best is to boost his/her ego in the way you know that he/she likes best.

Annie always moaned her appreciation whenever her man touched sensual spots and as he touched the places where she felt best, she emphasised 'Oh, that's where it's good, that's where it's best. Oh, that's marvellous. Just go on, rubbing there, that's wonderful right there', in a skilful combination of natural-sounding delight and masturbation instruction. What she didn't do was say anything negative (such as 'not there. That's the wrong place, can't feel a thing there') and therefore she avoided being discouraging.

It helps if your genitals are slippery. If you are not sexually excited enough to produce your own lubricant, it's a good idea to use spit, yes, plain old ordinary saliva. And if your partner doesn't think of it, then *you* must. There's nothing very difficult in transferring saliva on your hand to your genitals, and explaining that it makes everything feel better. If at any stage you experience fears at being so 'apparently forward' console yourself with the thought that you are only seeming forward to *yourself*, to your partner you are appearing as a knowledgeable but loving woman. There's nothing wrong with knowing what to do.

One move you can make is lovingly to guide your partner's fingers over the area that feels best, to give him/her an accurate idea of location, pressure and type of movement. In case this sounds obvious and silly, some lovers, however much they are willing to please, are themselves nervous and lacking in confidence. This doesn't mean they won't be glad to be helped to learn. It simply means you're doing them a favour by teaching them.

Kate eventually showed Ian how she masturbated herself so that he could see what she liked and how she needed it. Elaine's boy friend understood from a similar demonstration just *how long* Elaine needed vibration, something he'd not taken in previously.

What if, with the best will in the world, you can't seem to get the method across? It could be that you're not explaining, *in enough detail*, exactly what it is, when you touch yourself, that turns you on. Think carefully to see if you've left out some ingredient.

THE THREATENED LOVER

What happens if your partner feels threatened by your attempts to instruct? Don't give up, but don't let up. Temper your teaching methods with constant reassurance and words of love and appreciation. If you consistently, again and again, demonstrate with caring loving affection how marvellous you think he/she is, in time he/she will come round to understanding your needs.

Your partner will learn that in return for giving you great physical pleasure, he/she is being psychologically rewarded with renewed and reinforced love and affection. Sooner or later therefore he/she is going to stop feeling threatened and start feeling effective.

Suppose you struggle on, hammering out the love and affection, and months later you still haven't got anywhere with your reassurance? Your partner still apparently feels too threatened to be willing to learn and therefore to try and satisfy you?

This takes you beyond the realm of a sex problem to where, instead, you have reached a personality dispute. If there are enough other aspects of the relationship to make it worth continuing, even without any real sexual input on your partner's side, then naturally it will be worth relying on the vibrator to satisfy your sexual needs. If, however, your partner's inability to learn devastates your hopes of a good relationship, it may be that this partner, sadly, is the wrong one for you. A bad relationship in bed may be a reflection of a bad relationship outside it.

I used to think this a rather high handed attitude until I heard more and more stories from women in our workshops who were so obviously there, *not* because *they* had problems, but because their men did.

Jan and Jim are good examples of two people who were wrong for each other. Their difficulties and resentments showed up, above all, in the bedroom. Since leaving Jim two years ago, Jan has had two other relationships, both of which have been far better in every way.

Very often women who come for marriage or sex counselling are non-responsive in bed *because they're with the wrong partner*. It takes a lot of talking and working out to understand this and a lot more to actually do something about it. Since marriage problems are outside the range of the pre-orgasmic group and therefore of this book, the best thing to do in these circumstances is to find a good marriage counsellor and work out what's best for you.

MASTURBATION WITH INTERCOURSE

Once your partner has learnt how to bring you to climax, either by hand or with a vibrator, you have probably established a highly satisfactory sexual relationship. I personally think this kind of togetherness can be as good as a relationship that includes having orgasms during intercourse. But a lot of heterosexual people don't feel the same way. For them the ultimate is to satisfy each other sexually during intercourse.

The next step, therefore, for those who fall into this camp is to include masturbation with sexual intercourse. Yes, I know it promises broken wrists and all manner of uncomfortable positions, but it can be done very comfortably *once you get used to it*. Listen to what David has to say.

'We like lovemaking with me on top of her in the good old missionary position. We both enjoy this a lot but the only way she can come is by my including my fingers at a certain stage in the proceedings. I slip my right hand in between our bodies and with my forefinger pointing down along her legs, begin to massage her clitoris while my penis is going in and out of her very slowly. I move my hand much more firmly than my penis and I can keep going like that for a long time without it getting uncomfortable. If my body weight gets a bit much for only one arm to support, I sit back while my penis is still inside her, and can thus get even better access to her clitoris.

'Working out what's best for you has got to be a very individual thing. Some positions you simply can't keep up, but with a certain amount of trial and error to begin with it didn't take us long to find out what was comfortable.'

SELF-STIMULATION DURING INTERCOURSE

Some women prefer to use their own fingers rather than their partner's, and like masturbating themselves to orgasm during intercourse. But what about the women who need that extra added bit to really get going?

VIBRATORS DURING INTERCOURSE

The popular image of vibrators tends to be that they are for women only. Men, faced with a powered plastic penis rather easily feel rejected. But what most of us seem to have forgotten is that a vibrator can be very exciting for a man to use too. The vibrations on sensitive male skin, expecially on the scrotum, near the anus, at the base of the penis and on the sides of the penis itself, feel delicious. Some vibrators are manufactured for men.

The most devastatingly simple method therefore of giving each of you pleasure is not with some supersonic special gadget designed for both sexes. It's just a matter of wedging a plain, ordinary vibrator at a tactical point between your genitals (obviously where it is likely to give maximum stimulus to the clitoris) while you are actually making love. David sometimes uses this method with his girl friend too.

'It never fails,' he says. 'It can sometimes take her ages to come the other way, but this works almost instantaneously. To make sure the vibrator stays in position between us, I lean forward a bit more so that my weight is always gently pressing it on to her. If it's not in quite the right position, she will move it so that it improves.'

Lesbian women don't need advice about masturbation during intercourse. But the wedging-the-vibrator-between-the-bodies technique is one that would be just as useful for two women making love together.

David's point about the vibrator working where other methods have failed is an important one. American research into the speed of vibrators has discovered that the higher the speed of the vibrator the easier it is for the woman to climax. Some women, it appears, need a particularly high speed for their orgasm reflex to occur. To those women I would recommend investing in a mains operated vibrator. They are always more powerful than the battery operated ones and therefore more effective.

In 1977 I questioned thirty female vibrator users, ages ranging from twenty-two to sixty-six, in an attempt to discover what women felt about the vibrator and its relationship to intercourse. Slightly more than half said they were as satisfied or more satisfied with a vibrator-induced orgasm as with an orgasm induced by intercourse. About a third were less satisfied, and a small number either said 'it depends' or said the question didn't apply.

Slightly over half the group used the vibrator for penetration (not necessarily regularly but occasionally); slightly under half did not.

Sixteen women had used the vibrator on a partner and out of all the respondents only seven were able to climax *only* by masturbation while three of those were only able to climax with a vibrator.

The survey sample was too small to do anything other than provide general indications. What did become clear though was that for them, the vibrator was a welcome and diverting aid in relationships. It helped out when the regular partner was away, it solved orgasm problems with women who could have them by no other method and it provided variety.

ADDITIONAL READING

For couples with additional problems who need more help than is available in this book Paul Brown and Carolyn Faulder have written an excellent self-help sex book, *Treat Yourself to Sex* (Penguin). This includes specific sex therapy exercises that couples can carry out together to enhance and improve their love life.

PRE-ORGASMIC FOLLOW UP

What is your success rate? is a question I'm often asked by women who are thinking of coming to the groups. It's a difficult one to answer because success is not just measured in 'orgasms achieved'; success may also be a question of 'understanding lack of orgasms'.

Out of eighteen women attending recent groups, none of whom could climax, twelve learnt how to, six didn't. In addition a further eight women attended because they wanted to learn to have orgasms with their partners – a far more complicated and difficult ambition, and not, originally, something these groups were designed for. But . . . four of the eight did manage it occasionally and the other four began to feel it didn't matter nearly as much as they'd previously thought. Since other parts of their lives had improved as a result of attending, the group could therefore be said to be successful for them, in a less quantifiable way.

From time to time I send out follow-up forms to past members, with these sorts of results:

Anne: 'I could always masturbate to orgasm but only once in my life have I come through fucking alone. The assertion exercises were what helped me . . . I realised that clitoral stimulation could go along with fucking and that way I could come with my partner inside me.

'One minor but rather nice problem. I can come within a couple of minutes of contact now, so we don't bother making love for four or five hours any more and I miss it. Any hints for getting over laziness?! PS We achieved simultaneous orgasm the other night after I'd already come three or four times. Thank you!'

Pat: 'The group helped me by making me think and feel more positively about myself. It also made me realise that I have to work on *me* to bring out my sexuality.' (Pat learnt to masturbate, using a vibrator which she now also uses when making love with her partner.)

Gwen: 'I was extremely depressed and thought the group might help (it did). During the massage I was able to feel another person's hand on my body which I had been incapable of before. I became much better at receiving and demanding sexual pleasure. I did not feel like an outcast any more, but part of this world again, and I was not depressed any more.'

Elaine: 'Learnt how to use a vibrator. Can come easily with that. Think I've come mildly with boy friend while he was masturbating me. Still feel nothing or very little by touching myself.'

Mandy: 'I always fantasise or read or look at some sort of pornography. I also sometimes draw pornographic pictures while lying on my stomach and somehow pressing my pubic bone on the ground using a circular movement of the hips. I do have slight orgasms during intercourse fairly regularly now. I feel that I probably could have done even better had the relationship I was involved in been going better generally.'

Liz: 'I have had three or four orgasms which is very nice. But I only get them when I'm very relaxed. And I only feel this after a couple of drinks. And I don't drink very often as I once had a drink problem. So it's a dull life for Lizzie!

'It would be lovely if I could respond sexually without the aid of intoxicants. But it seems as if without them I am unable to get past the block I have. I think the block is a mixture of fear and also a hangover from my guilt-ridden, pleasure-taboo Presbyterian upbringing. But all in all things are better than they were before I started the group.'

KATE

Since much of the *after effect* of the group is as important as what happens during the immediate six weeks, I here reproduce, with her kind permission, Kate's diary. It's the same diary she started as part of her homework, but in her case, she carried on with it for six months after the group ended. Naturally all names of characters and places have been changed.

WEEK ONE
DAY ONE: 1. Mixed messages from parents – remember it was mother who encouraged sexuality and father who dampened it! Also mixed feelings that Ian is very sexually aware and anxious to have very good sex life. I feel pleased and anxious – *pleasure and pressure*.

2. Bio-energetics – face tensed as soon as I was asked to use the pelvic area.

3. Many dominant fathers around in the group.

4. I feel delighted with the group, relieved and excited. I'm surprised I'm looking forward to doing the exercises which I thought were boring before.

5. I'm worried about being able to stick to a whole hour a day on myself – on sheer physical experiences.

6. It's surprising mother told me so much about her sex life.

7. I feel I have a lot of sexual energy and I feel more hopeful and less embarassed.

8. I live through Ian's sexuality.

DAY TWO: I got into a mess with the staff group at work. Such pressure from a colleague that I was paralysed – I couldn't come out and be the aggressive self I can be. My colleague has given me a lot of talks, then pressure. Similarity to my father.

2. Did my vagina move a little when I did the grounding exercises?

3. Vagina alive after playing squash due to relaxed state.

4. Little more awareness of vagina while self-pleasuring.

DAY FOUR: Very low spirits. Ian is paralysed over an emotional decision. I am paralysed sexually.

DAY FIVE: Thought about times in bed with mother. Did she want to do more than just caress my back? I realise my mother enjoyed and was pleased when I became sexual (about 11–12 years old).

WEEK TWO

DAY ONE: Felt fine until demonstration – warmer after massage – gave me some confidence doing massage on strange body.

YES to Ian (sex) if I feel like it. NO to being controlled by Ian. NO to Ian in being as available as before and in returning to the old arrangement. YES to another man if the feeling comes up. Sebastian? YES to a Duke Ellington record. NO to driving carelessly when I'm angry or depressed.

EVENING AFTER SECOND GROUP MEETING: Ian: 'If you were ten years younger and had bigger tits, I'd marry you tomorrow.'

Next day: he says, 'I'm coming round to it.'

WEEKEND: Evening with friends. I thawed out, behaved naturally, and managed to do a massage on Sebastian while the others still there. I *received* his loving, very moving, wanted to cry, felt warm, trusting – did not lead to sex, but very positive – relaxed, non-titillating honest relationship.

Feel much more OK and pleased with my body taking a bath. Managed to talk to a girl friend about my real fears – very consoling.

Very fascinating, looking at the genitals. Where does the penis disappear to? Not pretty, like a wound in the body. Clitoris yes, labia yes, but the rest of it? How can something so open and vulnerable-looking remain protected?

Much happier, though, on the whole. It's very healthy and clean.

I'm going through enormous emotional changes. I have a much more positive contact with others, the whole world seems to have changed. Cried coming back home from the country, so moved by Hugh's kiss goodbye.

WEEK THREE
1. I SHOULD stand up for myself at all times.
   I SHOULDN'T be trodden upon.
2. I SHOULD be less heavy with Ian while keeping up my stand.
   I SHOULDN'T give up.
3. I SHOULD be optimistic.
   I SHOULDN'T put others first when feeling guilty.

For nearly two weeks Ian has been testing my change by asking again and again if I would go back to the same old routine. It's been no and no and no – and very wearying – I feel very disappointed and so frustrated with him. He's been using emotional blackmail to get me to return.

'I want you all the weekend . . . in that case I'll find another woman.'

I dreamt I couldn't stand up to my assistant in the office, woke up twice with a very powerful tension in my vaginal muscles – then realised I could cope with her. No problem with her at all the next day.

WEEK FOUR
Had orgasms with the vibrator. Delicious – but not as intense as the ones in my dreams. Betty Dodson's book is fabulous, as are her drawings – I feel my cunt to be beautiful. I've seen it before as dirty and infected.

1. I SHOULD stand up for myself.
2. I SHOULD control myself when I get worked up (bitchy).
3. I SHOULD let go when I'm enjoying myself.
4. I SHOULD drive the car more often after parties to let Ian have a good time i.e. I should let *him* go more.
5. I SHOULD keep hold of my feelings and not get so oppressed by others eg. work.
6. I SHOULD be more appreciative of what others do.

WEEK FIVE
1. I must look at my vagina again in the speculum. The association with dirt and disease is going.
2. Haley has not been hooked to women since having a woman lover.
3. Using the vibrator again will not limit me in other directions.

DAY THREE: Woke up feeling good. Later, I looked at Ian's magazines in bed for a 'game'. Did the Kegel exercises, then used the vibrator – mild orgasms – woke up feeling good.

DAY FOUR: Stood up to my pushy colleague at the office meeting – love and support followed from the others. Kegel exercises improving.

ONE WEEK AFTER GROUP ENDED

Since the group ended I have failed to come to the vibrator. Bought new batteries. I should control myself when I get angry and frustrated with Ian but still sustain my point of view.

1 Go back to bathing and relaxation of muscles.

2 Decided to look at genitals while using vibrator with a mirror. Success. Saw contractions in the mirror – had an exquisite orgasm. Why am I not more randy for Ian? By having his body inside me sexual desire seems to reach a plateau.

TWO WEEKS AFTER THE GROUP ENDED

Masturbated myself in front of Ian with the vibrator again, so exquisite – Ian keen to give me orgasms.

NEXT DAY

Reunion of four members of the group. Jo is confident I will come manually without the vibrator. Came again afterwards with the vibrator – facial muscles more relaxed – at a time of depression. Work colleague teasing me – yet I'm more together than usual. Wrote to my doctor to tell him my success story instead of my father.

THREE WEEKS AFTER THE GROUP ENDED

YES to putting myself first in the discussion about going to Cairo. And NO to going to Cairo and living together without deciding on marriage beforehand. Ian's relatives are in Cairo and he felt it was a big move to take me – tried to seduce me with the idea that this could take the place of a marital commitment. Made love to Ian that morning – he was passive after *he* had come, and he lost interest. He was very unstimulated by holding the vibrator to help me come, he left me in the middle of things to phone someone back – after *he* had come. And he didn't bother to disguise that he was anxious to get things ready for the arrival of our friends. I was unable to come as usual with the vibrator. Was it the atmosphere or was it the batteries? It was the former.

THREE MONTHS AFTER THE GROUP ENDED

I've tried to increase the number of different kinds of moods I'm in when trying to come to orgasm. Depressed, indifferent, moderately interested in sex. I'm still able to come, less intensely though and it takes longer. I still need vaginal stimulation. This seems to help me come more quickly. Tried it when Jean was in the other bed. Came in a woman's presence.

I now want to learn to move my body more, when expressing other things. I want to use sexual movement. Now I hope to increase other expressions. A dancer visited our unit the other day – a beautiful mover – fell in love with using the body.

I *no longer* live through Ian's sexuality. Several people have noticed a change in me.

FOUR MONTHS AFTER THE GROUP ENDED
Ian is now beginning to show interest in sharing the vibrator and allowing me to use it during intercourse. I'm near to coming while he's inside me – this is my next and dearest wish.

A WEEK LATER
Ian's word about the timing of his moving in has again and again proved empty. Tonight I told him that I was worried about another bad time if I said 'yes' (giving in to *his* needs) to his coming round. Angrily he told me he would contact me after he'd given his flatmate notice of his leaving. When this has been done I feel I will be able to support him during his seven-day-a-week working. He'd been saying one thing to his flatmate and another to me about leaving his flat.

SIX MONTHS AFTER THE GROUP ENDED
Mother died in November. I am closer to my father and Ian has moved in. At first the death of my mother and the practicalities of Ian's move took my energies away. Since a very hectic social life over Christmas and the New Year we've had more space to ourselves – fear about losing my independence is going.

At first I worried about never having time to myself in bed when I can use the vibrator – now I'm not so worried. Ian stays with his father sometimes – I always use it then. And I think he (we) are beginning to get over the embarassment of my need for it.

I no longer orgasm in dreams. I no longer dream about women, breasts etc. Instead I fantasise in my waking life. I'm happy to have erotic images of men now – and sometimes men only – women don't always figure in my fantasies.

A WEEK LATER
Last night I *made* Ian sit before me and told him to watch me masturbate while I used the vibrator. I couldn't believe he would remain indifferent (as he has done so far) to my coming with it. I told him 'you watch me and I will give you a massage afterwards'. He got quite turned on. Hurrah. After six months – at last my sexiness with the vibrator has affected Ian. Today we made love in the big chair. It

was good. I have just signed on for a massage course, as a way of giving me confidence in physical contact, not only sexuality, and opening up my physical caring life with others.

POSTSCRIPT: Eleven months after the group ended
The massage course helped me to make the bridge between companionship/friendship with sex – as I am more confident to touch people physically now and I express my affection that way. Before the massage course I felt that physical contact would lead inexorably to sex, and of course that is a crazy notion.

As Ian became more mixed up than ever about whether he wanted marriage or not after he moved in, I decided to make a stand and insisted on his leaving – he's tried many times to resume the relationship but I feel there's no point in wasting my time over him unless he wants to marry. And I've been able to carry on being assertive with him over this. This is the first time in my life I've been able to take this kind of stand with a man. Better late than never! I'm sure it's due to at last feeling confidence in myself – as a woman, an individual and with the realisation I'm truly a sexual being.

I'm still not orgasmic in intercourse but I feel hopeful that as I've changed so much in such a short space of time since the course that there's room for further change. It still makes me sad when I hear from women who are living with their partners that they orgasm in lovemaking. Sometimes I wonder if the reason I'm not living with or married to someone is because of my inability to come with a man; then I realise there are many women already living with lovers or husbands who don't either. But personally, I feel unless this happens, a relationship is under an enormous strain – I think I should go on another sexual workshop course to develop my sexuality further.

Change is the key word. The old fashioned concept that, once set on a certain path of behaviour, women could *never* change has been proved wrong. Kate's diary is an excellent example of this. This change can be triggered off by many things, a workshop, a book, a chance remark, a discussion, a traumatic event. But it's never too late. As the sixty-six-year old woman who responded to the vibrator survey said, 'too many people think anyone over the age of thirty-five is *kaput*.' As she made evident, you're never too old to begin enjoying sex, masturbation and vibrators. She tried her first vibrator at the age of 59.

CHAPTER 7
The four-week course

I wanted to find out, as an experiment, whether it was possible for the pre-orgasmic information to be absorbed successfully in less than six weeks. So recently I held a four-week course which was attended by six women. My notes, written each Thursday after our group session, show (I think) that four weeks can be as effective as six weeks, providing that use of the vibrator is emphasised much earlier on. I introduced it here in the second week.

STRUCTURE OF THE FOUR WEEK COURSE

Week One: Introduction. Give out homework sheets.
Week Two: Massage. Distribute *Liberating Masturbation* and vibrators.
Week Three: Talk about fantasies, suggest erotic reading material.
Week Four: Self-help demonstration. Discuss physiology of the climax and health. Sell speculums and the self-help guide.

HOMEWORK FOR WOMEN'S FOUR-WEEK SEXUALITY GROUP

Aim for one hour every day

WEEK ONE
Day 1: Getting comfortable with yourself and your body. Take a bath or shower, soap yourself slowly and sensuously, dry yourself and rub cream or lotion (baby lotion is good and cheap) slowly all over your body. (If you don't have access to a bathroom, just do the self-massage with cream.) Notice the different textures of skin and muscle. Take your time, enjoy yourself, get to know your body!
Day 2: 'Talk' your way through your body in front of a mirror. Note down your feelings about yourself in your diary.

Day 3: Spend today concentrating on the exercises previously described. (Relaxation and bio-energetics.)

Day 4: Write your diary. Repeat the breathing and bio-energetics exercises, doing the TENSE-RELAX pattern all through your body.

Day 5: Same as Day 1. Only this time, after touching your body, touch the genitals. Explore the sensation; find out what kinds of touch you like and what you dislike.

Day 6: Spend the hour indulging yourself – play music; dance. Write your diary, focus on anything you want to discuss at the group tomorrow.

WEEK TWO

Relaxation and breathing and bio-energetic exercises as before. In addition: YES/NO EXERCISE (three of each during week).

Day 1: Bath and self massage as before (Day 5 Week 1). Write your diary paying attention to your reactions to last night's meeting.

Day 2: Using a small mirror, take some time looking at your genitals. Can you identify the different parts? How do you feel about them; how do you feel looking at yourself? End session with breathing exercise.

Day 3: Diary: notice how you feel about your body and genitals. Where do you think your attitudes and feelings about your body have come from? Have they changed as you've grown older?

Day 4: Using your mirror, draw a sketch of your genitals. Look at the portraits in *Liberating Masturbation* if you have it.

Day 5: Self massage, spending more time on the genitals (as in Day 6, Week 1). Take plenty of time, don't aim for orgasm. Just pay attention to any feeling you have, however small. The aim is to build on these slowly, remake connections which have been disconnected for ages.

Day 6: Same as Day 5 Week 1, only use the vibrator to explore your body and genitals as well.

WEEK THREE

Do the Kegel exercises daily.

Tense your PC muscles, hold for count of five, relax. Repeat twenty times (Try to do this three times a day). Flutter exercise. Contract and relax the muscles quickly, ten times. Three times a day.

Going up and down in the lift (see Chapter 3). Three times a day.

Day 1: Bath and self massage, as Day 6, Week Two, including use of the vibrator. Record in your diary your reactions to last night's meeting.

Day 2: Continue with genital exploration: take plenty of time, don't aim for orgasm, just pay attention to any feelings you have.

Experiment with different pressures. Note down in your diary how you feel about this and any resistance you may feel.

Day 3: Repeat the breathing and bio-energetic exercises. Try to notice body tension building up, especially in the legs and thighs. Also try using different breathing pattern.

Day 4: Make a list of SHOULD/SHOULD NOTS. Ten of each. Write your diary with particular emphasis on how you feel when using your vibrator, noticing what your physical reactions are, as well as your mental reactions.

Day 5: Bath/self-masturbation, go on to masturbation work. Use either hand or vibrator as you prefer and give yourself at least thirty minutes on this. If you get bored or fed up, give yourself a short break and then continue. (It takes many women up to an hour of continuous stimulation to reach orgasm at first.)

Day 6: Repeat any of the homework you've enjoyed most. Re-examine your SHOULD and SHOULD NOTS. Are you happy with them? Where did they come from? Do they work for or against you?

EPILOGUE
Group dynamics

With each group, my methods as a group leader have changed. I've ended up by being much more directive than when I began. At first, Eleanor Stephens and I felt that all discussion should come un-prompted from the group and that the leaders should keep a low profile. As I went on to do more courses, I've realised that while the concept of the group, not the leader, 'doing the work' is vital, at the same time it's a fact that the leader is looked to for information and steering skills; skills to bring out problems that are difficult to talk about, skills to get a 'lazy talker' to say something important and therefore effectively to confront herself. I've learnt that in order to do this I need to play a far more active part in the proceedings than I'd originally planned.

The pre-orgasmic course is structured, with a great deal of in-formation to be disseminated at natural points in the conversation. What is important for a new group just starting is to realise that one or two people must prepare the information necessary for each week and that she or they must be responsible for that session. It doesn't work very well if there is no leader. Of course each group and its leader is going to work differently from the way I've laid out in the six-week course in this book. The contents are intended as a supply of in-formation and as a guideline both for individual women and for groups of women who feel the need to set up their own sexuality groups.

HOW TO RUN YOUR OWN GROUP

Arrange to use a particular room or flat on a regular basis for the extent of the course. It's a good idea to ensure the continuity of your meeting place since the group participants will quickly feel at ease.

Have a preliminary planning meeting with your friends during which, after studying this book, each of you decides to take responsibility for one particular week. If you need any special aids or reference books make sure they are available at the beginning of each meeting.

If certain subjects come up in the weekly meetings that the group leaders feel unsure of, use the index of this book to find the appropriate references and suggest that the group studies and discusses them.

The leaders of the weeks that include the massage and the self examination should, with a partner, practise everything that will need to be demonstrated *before* the meeting so that they have a good idea of what they're supposed to be doing at the time.

The following brief synopses of each week should give an idea of what to prepare and when to present the information.

WEEK ONE
While you are waiting for everyone to assemble for the first time, hand out some coffee or tea to put people at ease. You can do this at the beginning of each meeting. Suggest that each writes down on a piece of paper (provide paper and pens) their personal details, including name, address, where they can be reached by telephone, if they are living with anyone (if so, whom?) if they have ever experienced orgasm (if so, by what method?) and if they have ever masturbated. This information is to be collected and kept as useful reference material for each leader in turn. It also gives the women something useful to do at a time when otherwise they might be feeling nervous and tense. The beginning of the first meeting is also a good time to give out all the homework sheets (pre-prepared) for the following weeks. Stress the importance of religiously doing the homework for one hour a night for the next five weeks.

When everyone is assembled, do the exercise described in Chapter 1, each talking to a partner for five minutes, and then go round the circle, each one in turn, saying who you are, why you are at the group, what sexual relationships you have at present, what kind of relationship your parents appeared to demonstrate when you were a child and what kind of messages you received from them during teenage about sexuality, either verbally or from your parents' attitudes towards sex.

The leader will find that, quite naturally, certain subjects will come up, like for example, the desire to have an orgasm *at the same time as a partner*, the belief that a clitoral orgasm is inferior to a vaginal one. This is where she needs to step in and provoke discussion on these subjects using *The Body Electric* as an information service and a guide. If the subjects underlined and stressed in Chapter 1 *don't* naturally come up in conversation it's the job of the leader to make sure that they're covered by bringing them in herself. (This is where the preliminary preparation is vital.)

Each session should last for two-and-a-half to three hours and the last third of Week One should be spent on practising the exercises for the homework, together. (Again, the leader will have worked these out in advance.)

It's important to set a time limit for each session and to stick to it otherwise the people who have to leave early will miss out on valuable discussion.

Encourage each other to ask questions, to chip in with information and contributions. Tell the group to bring towels and oil to the next meeting.

WEEK TWO
Spend the first half of the meeting taking it in turns to discuss how each of you has got on with the homework. It may be useful to read from your diaries. If there have been difficulties in doing the exercises, go through them again. This week's leader should pick up on the specific topics that will arise from the homework discussion and should air them in the same way as last week's leader did, using the book as a guide and reference. This applies to every session and every leader. If points stressed in Chapter 2 *don't* naturally arise this is where the leader must include them on her own initiative.

The second half should be devoted to the massage. First of all, give the demonstration on a pre-arranged assistant, then pair up the couples and get them to set to. If some people are shy of taking their clothes off explain that there is absolutely no pressure to do so. Invariably when they get down to the actual experience they feel so silly in their underclothes that they end up by taking them off anyway. Give each other an agreed twenty minutes of massage each. Try and leave ten minutes at the end in which to go through next weeks homework together, explaining anything new.

WEEK THREE
Spend the first half of the meeting talking about the homework. Don't forget to include any missing subjects. Devote the second half to the self-examination. The leader should demonstrate it, a pre-arranged partner should follow suit and then the other women should be encouraged, though not pressurised, to do likewise. Discuss the self-help information and talk about your own sexual health. Discuss the methods of contraception used by each group member, people's attitudes to abortion, menstruation, VD etc. Go through next week's homework, explaining anything new.

WEEK FOUR
In the first half of the session, talk about how you are getting on with the homework, what has happened to each of you in your

relationships and jobs since starting the group. Distribute the vibrators (orders taken in the previous week) and talk about how to include them in the homework.

The second half of the meeting should be the leader's description of the physiology of orgasm, the woman's sexual response cycle (see Chapter 4). Go through next week's homework if necessary and ask each group member to write down her sure-fire sexual fantasy during the week in order to bring to the next meeting.

WEEK FIVE

First half: talk about homework with special concentration on people's experience with the vibrator. Second half: talk about the use of fantasies. Shuffle the fantasies used as part of last week's homework, and read them out to each other, discuss their implications and effectiveness. Talk about keeping a menstruation diary and ways of improving relationships with partners.

WEEK SIX

Treat this final week as a party. Bring some drink and something nice to eat.

Talk about homework and general progress. Do a farewell massage together. A foot massage is a nice one to celebrate with and can be prepared by this week's leader from *The Art of Sensual Massage* by Inkeles and Todris (George Allen and Unwin).

GROUP VALUE

The main strength of these grass roots courses is that they are held *by* women *for* women. Talking about sexuality and learning how to masturbate (in particular getting familiar with vibrators) is not something that needs a medical degree or social work qualification. It's something women can easily do for themselves.

A minority of women have *not* learnt to climax from the exercises and information set out here. Some have been women without enough motivation to learn who have not apparently been upset at their resulting lack of climax. Some have had a great deal of motivation and consequently do need follow-up help after the final week. It is important that these women should be helped subsequently to find a good counsellor. The National Marriage Guidance Council can help, and most Area Health Authorities have psychological services which would also be of assistance.

But the majority of women do learn, and find that their lives are subsequently enriched. There is no one particular aspect of the course that can be isolated as *the* catalyst that always clicks. For some it was the massage, for others the assertion techniques, or it may have been straightforward sex instruction.

It's for this reason that I haven't written a simple chapter called 'How to Masturbate'. If learning self-confidence or touching is as important as the self-stimulation itself, women will emerge from this book or from a group run along these lines with a broader sense of what constitutes a *whole* woman and will understand better how that person affects those immediately around her.

What begins at the group can have repercussions like the ripple spreading from a pebble tossed into a lake. An example of this on one level is the character that Jan (in this book) is based on. The real woman *did* rather nervously advertise, as Jan did. She *had* been physically 'hooked' on her unsuitable lover and was very lacking in self-confidence.

Her ad produced 'an alcoholic rock musician but he *was* beautiful'. This new lover was only destined to live with Jan for six months. But he did have the effect of teaching Jan she could indeed be attracted to someone other than the man she'd been fixated on. So when she eventually met a third person, she not only knew more about her sexuality, she'd developed confidence and was actually looking foward to the sexual side of the friendship. This is the man with whom she's been living happily ever since.

On a more dramatic level, there is the case of Lucy, who changed her entire life. She changed her job, her accommodation and her boyfriend. As well as learning to value herself as a woman, she was able for the first time to be effective in the world that existed around her. As a result of learning to prize herself, she developed her social consciousness as a woman.

Was it merely coincidence that Lucy experienced an immediate ability to orgasm? Today, two years later, Lucy can orgasm with or without the vibrator and can quite happily do so with her lover. Her relationship with this lover is possibly the best one she's ever enjoyed. It's good enough for the pair of them to want to set up home together. Nicholas had known Lucy earlier in her life, before she joined the pre-orgasmic workshop. 'From being uncertain, clinging, full of fears and inferiorities, she's turned into a balanced, attractive capable woman who is independent and self-supporting.' Can't be bad, can it?

INDEX

additional reading, 24, 40, 58, 73, 81, 94
adult retraining, 76

bio-energetic exercises, 22
bisexuality, 80
breaking up a relationship, 48

cervical smears, self-examination, 55
clitoris, 16, 28ff; during lovemaking, 71; hooded, 72; stimulation during intercourse 29; indirect stimulation, 71
counselling, outside the group, 118

discharges, and self-examination, 55

excitement, 68

faking, 13
fantasies, 82ff
Forum, 43

group dynamics, 115
groups, how to run, 115; value of, 118

human sexual response cycle, female, 68

intercourse, with mutual masturbation, 103; with self-stimulation, 103; with vibrators, 104
IUDs, during self-examination, 55

Kegel exercises, 58, 59

libido, unequal, 93
living alone, 48
lonely hearts advertising, 99
lovemaking, 100ff; communicating with lover, 100; threatened lover, 102

massage, 30ff; as communication, 32; as therapy, 32; how to, 35
masturbation, 16ff; during intercourse, 103; how women do it, 72; mutual with intercourse, 103; myths of, 20; value of, 18; what it is, 16
meeting people, 49
menstruation, 18; diary, 90; menstrual cycle, 90; self-examination during 54; speculum and signs of, 54
multiple orgasms, 71
muscle tension, 69
myths, of masturbation, 20, 71; of sexuality, 16

nudes, and the media, 30

open marriage, 66
orgasm, 19, 21, 70ff; multiple, 71; myths of, 21; physiology of, 68; safeguard against aggression, 20; selfishness of, 21; simultaneous, 71

plateau phase, 70
pre-orgasmic women, results, 105
pregnancy, 54–55
privacy, the value of, 44

relaxation-tension exercises, 22–24
resolution phase, 71

satisfaction, 20
self confidence, 17
self-image, 30
self-examination, 50ff; value of, 51; group, 52; and the speculum, 53
selfishness, value of, 3, 25
sex aids, mail order, 73
sex contract, 44
sexism, teenage, 2, 14
sexual response cycle, 68
sexuality, myths of, 16, 71
SHOULD/SHOULD NOT exercises, 74ff
skin, genital, 56
speculum, how to use, 57; uses of, 54
stimulation, research on, 27
switch off, automatic, 21

uterus, retroverted, 56

vaginal gasp, 61
vibrators, 60; batteries for, 100; during intercourse, 29, 104; fears of, 76, 79; practice with, 96–97; versus fingers, 77; a survey of, 104

Wolff, Dr Charlotte, 81

YES/NO exercises, 40

NATURAL HEALING IN GYNECOLOGY
A User's Guide by Rina Nissim

'. . . compels us to care for our health in an
intelligent and truly preventive manner. It
provides a range of healing alternatives from
Eastern and Western cultures, and critiques the
limits of conventional Western medicine, giving
us the power of choice . . . An unusual and
valuable resource indeed.'
> *Boston Women's Health Book Collective*

192pp   illustrated

0 86358 069 6 pbk

BEING FAT IS NOT A SIN
Shelley Bovey

Being fat is not a sin, but, argues Shelley Bovey, the majority of overweight women are made to feel otherwise.

Pithy and controversial, this book cuts straight to the heart of the fat taboo and uncovers a deep-seated prejudice against fat women. Those who don't fit into society's strict limits on size are not just the butt of seaside postcards; they are considered stupid, incompetent and even deviant.

Shelley Bovey, herself a size 24, exposes discrimination in all its forms, and reveals that this is far more threatening to a woman's physical and mental health than the medical risks associated with being fat. She puts tough questions to Harley St. surgeons, dieticians and others with a vested interest in women wanting to be thinner, and talks to doctors who confess that prejudice, not scientific fact, makes them condemn fat women as 'unhealthy'.

Fat may be a feminist issue but for women who are size 16 and over it is often a miserable reality. Now they share experiences which will strike familiar chords in the heart of every woman who has ever worried about her weight.

Being Fat is Not a Sin helps find a way out of this isolation. It is about losing guilt and inhibition – not about losing weight.

MOTHERHOOD: WHAT IT DOES TO YOUR MIND   Jane Price

'Why didn't anyone tell me it would be like this?'

Having a child is as challenging mentally as it is physically but few of us are prepared for the confusing, often violent, emotions that come with motherhood.

This book is a radically new approach to the psychology of motherhood. Jane Price, herself a mother of two, draws on women's accounts of their feelings at every stage of pregnancy and early motherhood to help us towards a better understanding of those intense emotions which cannot simply be explained away as post-natal depression.

Anger, resentment, guilt and anxiety, jealousy if your baby likes somebody else, fear that you're not 'bonding' properly and an overwhelming sense of inadequacy can make even the sanest woman think she's losing her mind. Jane Price shows how our childhood image of what a mother is – or should be – influences every decision we make: when to have a child in the first place; whether to breastfeed; when, if at all, to return to work. She shows too why women struggle to be at least as good or a great deal better than their own mothers – and why they *think* they fail. Weighing the expectations of parents, partners and friends against our own and never losing sight of the real challenges of being a mother today, Jane Price helps us to accept ourselves – and others – as 'good enough' rather than perfect mothers. She points the way forward to a positive, growing relationship with our children, their father and our own parents.

Dr Jane Price is a psychiatrist and psychotherapist who specialises in the psychology of women.

0 86358 211 7   £4.95 pbk

WOMEN AND THE AIDS CRISIS
Diane Richardson

*'The book of the year, if not the decade' – Angela
Carter*

In this fully revised, up-dated and enlarged New
Edition of *Women and the AIDS Crisis*, Diane
Richardson gives us the latest figures and
research findings, recent developments in policy
on AIDS and a fully up-dated Resources Section
for Britain and Australia. She provides an
extended section on safer sex and racism, and
she includes further interviews with HIV
positive women and with carers of people who
have AIDS, illuminating how women today are
coping with the challenge of AIDS.

This brand new edition also explores those issues
that AIDS raises for pregnant women, for lesbians,
for women who use drugs and for prostitutes.

'This is the first well-documented book on
women and AIDS to appear in a form accessible
to the non-professional public. Diane
Richardson's approach is candid and her
research excellent. It is original, thought-
provoking and timely. Any reader who does not
emerge with a warmer compassion and
understanding of the problems must be a harsh
individual indeed.' – *Janet Green, Counselling
Administrator, Terrence Higgins Trust*

'. . . this is the one you should be reading – it
may turn out to be the only one you ever need to
read.' – *Rose Collis, City Limits*

'A strong counterblast to all the
misinformation.' – *Anna Raeburn*

'. . . her politics are inherent to her approach, her
feminism intrinsic and her style of writing
accessible to readers of all political persuasions.'
– *Amanda Hopkinson, New Statesman*

0 04 440357 7   £4.95

YOUR LIFE AFTER BIRTH
Exercises and Meditations for the First Year of
Motherhood
Paddy O'Brien

This positive and practical handbook draws on
women's own accounts of their post-natal
feelings and experiences, and provides a
comprehensive programme of relaxation,
guided fantasy, assertiveness and self-defence
to help you grow stronger – emotionally as
well as physically.

It provides practical, mental and physical
exercises to help you cope with tiredness and
the new demands on your time and emotions,
and to make positive plans for *yourself* as well
as the baby. It helps you to rediscover your
own needs and desires; to express your
feelings about the experience of having a child
and what this does to your body; and to make
realistic decisions about whether to have
another child. It also includes women's
moving accounts of their experiences of
stillbirth and one mother's feelings about the
challenge of caring for her handicapped child.

BIRTH AND OUR BODIES
Paddy O'Brien

This practical and positive companion guide
provides women with detailed physical and
mental exercises to practise through
pregnancy and birth.

Working chronologically from the time
when a woman may not even be pregnant but
hopes to conceive in the near future, right
through to the birth itself, the guide provides
a comprehensive exercise programme for
relaxation, combating morning sickness, stage
fright in the last few weeks of pregnancy and
for strengthening the pelvic floor muscles.

Illustrated with line drawings taken from
'life' both in the exercise classes which Paddy
O'Brien runs, and at the time of the birth
itself, BIRTH AND OUR BODIES helps
mothers to stay in touch with a body, and in
charge of it, when it seems in danger of being
taken over by the baby. So, as well as
maintaining and strengthening your muscles
you get stronger and more supple emotionally.

This is a pocket-sized companion, easy to
use at home, or at work – it encourages the
participation of partners and can be used too
whenever you have time to yourself.

FIT FOR THE FUTURE
The Guide for Women who want to live well
Jeanette Winterson

Fit for the Future is a complete manual for any woman who wants to live well.

It describes the pitfalls and pleasures of rebuilding your body as you would like it to be. Written by someone who did it herself, the book encourages an intelligent approach to getting fit that allows for individual temperaments and lifestyles and discourages the 'fitness robot' approach to health.

Fit for the Future includes:
Clear exercise and anatomy diagrams
A challenging look at the world of sport;
What are women good at and why?
What are the mental and physical benefits of various sports?
How to eat well and never diet again
How to improve your sex life

You owe it to yourself to be beautiful. This book offers no miracles. But it does demand that you concentrate on yourself and fulfil your own extraordinary potential.

Dear Paul

Here is one of the books recommended. It is as you see for women but would be readable for men also. The other 'female' book is Mirror Within Ann Dixon. Highly recommended & 'always on the shelf' in Smiths etc is The Joy Of Sex Paul Brown.

Other possibilities from my course on sex

Sexual Happiness: a practical approach
M Yaffe & E Fenwick — London Dorling Kindersley

Men & Sex B Zilbergeld 1980 Fontana.

I've written to the British Association for Counselling & asked

them to send you a list of
accredited therapists in your area.

Hope this is of some help

Good Luck

Mother!

P.S. Essay has been returned —
its too big & has to be cut down
to size. Ugh!.

PPS There's a good programe on
ITV Mondays 1040 — The Good Sex
Guide with addresses to write to plus
Book & Video to be on sale in bookshops
soon.